STARK RAVING BONKERS!

More Confessions of a Dog-Sitter
by Jane Mosse

2022

Published by Blue Ormer Publishing
for Bordeaux Barn Writers.
www.blueormer.co.uk

ISBN 978-1-7396814-4-9 (paperback)

For Richard

"*Everyone thinks they have the best dog.
And none of them are wrong.*"

W R Purche

PRELUDE

'So where are you two off to this time?' asks my brother one evening during one of our increasingly rare phone-calls.

'I'm not sure. I'm still waiting for confirmation but possibly Finland,' I reply calmly.

I can sense his eyes rolling even though it isn't a video call.

'Finland? Why on earth does anyone want to go to Finland Chris?' he splutters. 'It's riddled with midges and ticks. You'll get bitten alive and probably catch Lyme disease. Besides which it'll be bitterly cold. It isn't even as though you and Rob like skiing.'

'Oh stop overreacting! The insect population will be fast asleep in January.'

'So what are you looking after this time? A herd of reindeer?'

'No, a couple of forest cats and a Norrbotten,' I reply wearily.

'A Gnawbottom? What on earth's a Gnawbottom?' comes the exasperated response.

'It's a breed of dog native to Finland. Anyhow, we may not get selected so you can calm down. The sit's proving very popular, there are lots of people applying.'

'I can't imagine why. I find it hard to believe that there are even more people like you who are willing to travel halfway across Europe at their own expense and look after someone else's animals for free. You're stark raving bonkers, the pair of you.'

CLOUD CUCKOO LAND

IT'S JANUARY AND IT'S raining. In fact it's been raining for the last ten days. A thick blanket of mist has wrapped itself around the island and the fog-horn can be heard baying in the distance, its rhythmic blasts serving as a depressing reminder that we are all rock-bound here in Guernsey. No ferries or flights have been able to leave for the last three days as both rough seas and high winds have proved too challenging. Not even the supply boat has managed to get in, so the supermarket shelves are devoid of yoghurt and fresh veg is becoming a rarity.

'It's no good Chris. I'm going to go stir-crazy if it carries on like this,' announces Rob one afternoon. 'It's hardly surprising that so many people suffer from depression in January. I mean, look at it out there. There's a veritable moat round the front door and the garden's sodden. There's no point going for a drive or a walk because you can't see anything. Even if we did we'd risk being blown off a cliff.'

'Well read your book or write a poem or something,' I reply unsympathetically. 'Or you could make a start on decorating the spare room. You've been talking about it for months.'

'I've already read three books and it's only the 12th of January and I've run out of inspiration for writing. You know that the smell of paint gives me a migraine so there's no way I'm going to start any decorating if I can't even open the windows.'

It was never our intention to be at home for January but sadly a carefully-planned house-sit in Finland had had to be cancelled at the last minute due to the owners suffering a sudden family bereavement. So, instead of us luxuriating in 'a well-appointed lake-side house complete with sauna, two forest cats and a Finnish Norrbotten,' we found ourselves stuck at home suffering the worst weather we'd witnessed for months.

'Well, get on line and find us another house-sit,' I suggest encouragingly. 'It's a good time to do a search because lots of people will be going skiing or heading for the sun. And here, it's about time you did some of the donkey-work,' I say, passing Rob the iPad. 'Hopefully the weather will pick up in the next few days, it can't go on like this for much longer.'

'Where do you fancy going then?' asks Rob, settling down on the sofa. 'I'd rather avoid taking the car across the Channel. It's so expensive and you know I turn green just looking at the sea.'

I have to agree as Rob tends to spend most of any sailing trip throwing up in the loos.

'Well it's unlikely the ferries will be sailing and we really can't take the risk of being unreliable sitters. Why don't we try to be a bit more adventurous and fly somewhere? I know we've done a lot of sits since we signed up with the agency, but we haven't really ventured very far.'

'Mmm, I suppose you're right. I'll have a browse.'

As I settle down in my favourite armchair to read my novel there are various mutterings coming from Rob who, in his systematic way, is sitting with a pen and paper taking notes as he scrolls through the hundreds of requests for sitters on the web-site. With over a hundred and thirty countries to choose from I guess it could take him some time.

'Maybe we should go to America?' I suggest tentatively, already anticipating the reaction. 'I've always wanted to explore some of the National Parks. Or even better, we could go to New York.'

'No way. We might get mugged,' comes the immediate response.

'Oh Rob, don't be ridiculous, you think the whole of the US is full of crazy people. There are lots of safe areas and some really wonderful places to see.'

'No way am I going to the States. Anyhow, it's too far. I don't fancy doing any long-haul flights.'

'So I guess that rules out Australia or India then?'

'India? Why would I want to go to India? You know I hate Indian food and yes, of course it's too far.'

'But darling, you've only ever had an Indian take-away or an M&S meal deal. I'm sure that proper Indian cuisine would be really exciting.'

'I don't need food to be exciting Chris and I certainly don't want to spend my entire time eating curry. No, it's too far and I'd need to have all manner of injections. I'd probably get cholera or typhoid. Do you know Fred Trueman bowled his fastest overs ever when the England cricket team went to Delhi? He was desperate to get back to the loo.'

Two hours later we seem to have narrowed down our 'being more adventurous' to Europe.

'Well at least we'd be close enough to get home if anything awful happened,' muses Rob. 'But there is the language barrier.'

'Don't be silly. Everyone speaks English these days. I know it's lazy of us to expect everyone to speak our language but I can manage a bit of French and Italian and a smattering of German.'

'I didn't know you'd learned German,' replies Rob, peering at me over the top of his glasses and looking suitably impressed by my revelation.

'Well, I only did a year at school. It was because we'd got this new teacher, Mr Pugh. He looked just like that DJ with the floppy blonde hair, Simon Dee, and we all fancied him. He used to wear corduroy jackets and his wife used to make him matching ties and hankies out of flowery material.'

'Lucky you. My French teacher was a tiny shrew of a woman called Miss Willie. She was about four foot six and wore her hair scraped back in a bun. She looked about ninety. Needless to say she suffered horribly because of her name.'

'Poor woman. You're a bit of a dark horse yourself. I didn't realise you'd learned French.'

'Ha! It didn't do me much good. I gave up trying after I arrived in the centre of Paris and asked a nun where the war was.'

'The war? What war? Why on earth would you want to ask anyone where the war was?'

'I wasn't intending to, I got muddled that's all. I was trying to ask for the station but I got *gare* and *guerre* mixed up, and I called her Madame.'

'Oh Rob, you're impossible. Only you could manage a faux pas like that. Anyhow, have you found us anything interesting yet?'

'Well there's a sit in Holland that looks okay. Two pussy-cats and a rescue dog. Oh, and a bearded dragon. I missed that bit. No, I'll cross that one off the list. I'm not keen on reptiles. You have to feed them insects or dead mice don't you? Let's stick to mammals. Mmmm. Four sausage-dogs in Germany?'

'That's a lot of dogs. I think two is more than enough. Four sounds like hard work.'

'How about this one then? A dog and a tank of fish.'

'That sounds doable. Where is it? Anywhere exciting?'

'Switzerland.'

'Oh, that would be wonderful. It's such a beautiful country.' My imagination already has me wandering through beautifully manicured Alpine meadows with a back-drop of snow-clad mountains, bringing the goats home for milking and collecting the eggs each morning for breakfast. 'I don't know a thing about fish but you could manage those couldn't you?'

'Yes, I used to keep fish when I was younger so I could cope with that.'

'What sort of dog is it? A St Bernard?'

'No, it's a poodle.'

'A poodle? I thought it would be something big and hairy like a Bernese Mountain dog.'

'There's a photo of the dog here but it looks a bit odd. Come and have a look.'

'What's odd about it?' I ask, leaning over to get a closer look.

'Well it's got a silly sort of top-knot.'

'Ha, I see what you mean. What's its name?'

'Heidi.'

'Well that's original. But I agree, she does look a bit ridiculous with that silly pom-pom on her head but that's what people do with poodles. I know they're supposed to be very intelligent but it's hard to believe it when you see them looking like that. She reminds me of those loo-roll covers that my Nana used to knit. Mind you, she has got a pretty face. I'm game to give it a go. I imagine it would be fairly straightforward and there'll be snow at this time of year. But don't build your hopes up because it'll probably be a popular one with the skiing fraternity. They'll be inundated with applicants.'

Two weeks later, having successfully escaped the island, we're greeted by the distinctive sound of Alpen horns echoing through the valley and the rhythmic, dull clanging of cow-bells. The fact that we're still seated on the shuttle-train at Zurich airport makes us wonder what else the Swiss have dreamed up to welcome us. At the railway station we climb on board a spotlessly-clean train, its paintwork gleaming, for the short journey to our sit. Leaving the city behind precisely on time, we're soon travelling through the spectacular Swiss countryside. The lush, green fields in the valley look newly-mown, the foothills scattered with idyllic houses and chalets and behind them the snow-clad mountains make it all look every inch a picture-postcard.

Forty minutes later we arrive at our destination, tired after our journey but excited to see our new home. But this isn't one of the dream chalets on the slopes; it's an immaculate-looking dormer bungalow that sits in a rather smart, residential area just above the lake. The paintwork looks as though someone completed the final touches only yesterday, the lawn, which is surrounded by a well-tended shrubbery, sports regularly-mown stripes even though it's still January, and the roof of the building carries a huge bank of solar panels that looks efficient enough to provide enough power for the entire neighbourhood. Before we have the chance to ring the door-bell our hosts are at the door to greet us.

'Christine! Robert! Welcome to Switzerland!' says a rather tall, elderly gentleman with a smart, trimmed, white beard, whom we assume to be Theo. 'Please, please, come in.'

As we enter, we're greeted by a very small, dumpy lady who claps her hands together in excitement, beaming at us from behind a pair of very thick glasses.

'This is Elsbeth, my wife. We are very happy that you are coming. But please come in.'

As we walk into the hallway I catch Elsbeth glancing down in horror at our heavy footwear and casting a swift and imploring look at her husband.

'Oh, and if it is good with you then please we take shoes off in the house,' he says quickly.

'Oh, of course. I'm so sorry. These are our walking shoes. We'll leave them here in the porch if that's okay?' I suggest, smiling reassuringly.

'Er, I think maybe is better if we keep your shoes in another room. I will take them.'

As Theo shuffles off to the back of the house Elsbeth takes our coats and suggests, in perfect English, that we take our things straight up to our room and leads us upstairs.

'This is our guest room, I hope you like it. There's a beautiful view of the mountains and the lake from the window and you can watch the sun rise from behind the ridge in the morning.'

Her English is so perfect that I'm beginning to wonder if she is English.

'It's a lovely room Elsbeth,' replies Rob. 'I'm sure we'll be very comfortable.'

'Well, if you want to hang some of your things up I'll go down and make us all a cup of coffee and then you must meet Heidi. She'll be very excited!'

When our hostess is safely out of ear-shot we can't help having a fit of the giggles.

'Crikey, it's all a bit 'just so' isn't it?' remarks Rob. 'It's going to be a challenge keeping the place clean and tidy. Anyhow, let's leave our stuff and go down and meet our new charge!'

We return to the sitting-room but stand around dithering, wondering where we should sit. It's frighteningly tidy and is furnished with two large armchairs and a two-seater settee, all in white leather. Strangely the two armchairs are enveloped by heavy, clear plastic covers, the sort that furniture stores use to protect items when they're newly delivered. I can only assume that they're a recent acquisition. Various tables and a large dresser in ornately-carved, dark wood display a series of plates depicting trains and just inside the door hangs a traditional Swiss cuckoo-clock. On a large, polished sideboard sits a spotlessly-clean aquarium filled with various aquatic plants and a sunken pirate-ship through which weave several gaily-coloured fish of various sizes. It's altogether rather unusual and horribly immaculate. We sit down side by side on the sofa assuming that the two armchairs must be out of bounds. Suddenly, what feels like a rather awkward silence is relieved by the entry of our new charge: a large, white, standard poodle, who prances excitedly across the tiled floor closely followed by Theo.

'So, this is Heidi,' he beams, clearly proud of this rather glamorous powder-puff of a dog. 'She is our baby, aren't you *meine Liebling*?'

'Oh, she's beautiful,' I respond encouragingly as Heidi nuzzles at my hand, her snowy-white pom-pom wobbling slightly. 'How old is she?' I ask, fondling her head, obviously much to her delight. She feels wonderfully silky.

'She is three years old and she is very special dog. She is winning prizes,' Theo says proudly. 'We are showing her, and very soon we have important show in Zurich and we hope that she is winning.'

Oh my, so this is no common or garden poodle; we've landed ourselves a show-dog.

'The show is two days after we are returning,' Theo continues, 'so our, how you say, dog hairdresser, is coming to the house before we are getting back. I hope that is not a problem for you?'

'No, of course not,' I reply. 'That's no problem at all. How often do you have to have her trimmed Theo?'

'She must have cut every four or five weeks, but she loves it. I think all you ladies are liking the beauty treatment,' he laughs, smiling in my direction, his eyes twinkling.

I'm quietly wondering how many Swiss francs that will cost.

'Christine, Elsbeth will need to show you how to brush Heidi. It is vey important that her coat does not become er, how do you say in English?'

'I think you mean matted Theo. Yes, I've been reading about it. Their coat is very soft isn't it? It must be a lot of work to keep her looking so beautiful.'

'Oh yes. We brush her every day and when she goes out she must wear her coat and her boots.'

I can see Rob's jaw drop and know we're both thinking the same thing. Boots? We've had lots of dogs wearing coats but not boots. This could be interesting.

'It's because of the snow,' calls Elsbeth from the kitchen. 'People tend to use anti-freeze and they also treat the roads. All of those things are very bad for dogs. If they come home and lick their feet they can get poisoned.'

'I'd never thought of that,' says Rob, 'but of course, it makes sense. Does she mind wearing them?'

'No, not at all,' replies Elsbeth. 'She began wearing them when she was just a puppy so she's used to them.'

'So, Robert,' says Theo, 'if you would please come with me I will show you where we keep her food and I can also show you some things in the garage and the garden that you will need to know. Oh, and I must also show you the heating system.'

Rob casts me a look of slight alarm as he dutifully follows Theo out towards the back of the house. I can't help smiling as it tends to be me who takes on all the technical information, Rob not really being the engineer in our household. I don't like to intervene but hope that he manages to take notes during the guided tour.

'And if you come with me Christine, I can show you how to groom our little lady,' smiles Elsbeth.

An hour later Rob is still under instruction in the garage and, having had my own tuition session, I find myself sitting in the lounge while Elsbeth prepares the coffee in the kitchen. The silence is made somehow more intense by the monotonous ticking of the cuckoo clock. However, at four o'clock precisely, the little wooden doors open and a brightly-painted cuckoo emerges with great exuberance and, with Swiss precision, Elsbeth appears with a tray, beautifully laid with four fine china cups. She carefully pours me a coffee, places it on a pretty crocheted mat on the table beside me, then seats herself on one of the armchairs causing the plastic to crackle. In an effort to make conversation I ask her where it is they're going while we look after Heidi.

'We're going to Germany,' she smiles. 'Theo and I are members of a folk dance group and every year we go on a small tour together.'

'Oh how wonderful, that sounds like fun,' I reply, trying to sound enthusiastic. Fortunately it's at that moment that I catch the sound of the men returning. I can't help but overhear Theo who seems to be informing Rob of something important.

'Yes, I know, but in 1972 the Swiss Federal Railway is introducing a timetable so that trains are arriving and leaving the station at the same minute past every hour and then, in 1977, the *Gesamtverkehrskommission* is making a new line and we are having the trains that can go at 200 kilometres fast. 200 kilometres Robert!'

Rob glances in my direction, eyes rolling and I have to control my urge to laugh. As he and Theo sit down to join us (Theo taking the remaining crackly armchair) Heidi reappears, trotting into the room and heads straight for Rob's pocket.

'Ha! She is already knowing that you are hiding biscuits,' laughs Theo.

'You'll need to watch her,' interrupts Elsbeth. 'She's a terrible thief, aren't you Heidi?'

Hearing her name called, Heidi turns, goes over to Elsbeth, and attempts to climb on her knee but is immediately pushed away.

'*Nein Heidi, komm her!*' commands Theo.

'Does she understand English or do I need to learn some German?' asks Rob.

'No worries, she's bilingual,' laughs Elsbeth, 'though she might try it on and pretend not to understand you.'

'And your English is perfect Elsbeth. Where did you learn to speak so beautifully?' I ask, unable to contain my curiosity.

'My mother was English but my father was Swiss so I grew up bilingual. I've always spoken English with Heidi but she barks in German,' she laughs, looking fondly at the dog. 'Now, if you will excuse us, we must go and finish our packing. Please make yourselves at home.'

It's later that night when we've managed to make our excuses and headed for bed that we have the chance to exchange our findings.

'So, apart from a history of the Swiss Railways, what else did you find out?' I ask, curious to know the content of the garage discussions.

'Oh Chris, you're never going to believe it. It's going to take ages to explain everything. Talk about Swiss efficiency. That man is absolutely round the bend!'

'Why? What ever makes you say that?'

'Well, let's start with the rain gauge. The rain gauge, which hangs on the fence opposite the kitchen window, needs to be read at the end of each day and the reading recorded on the clipboard that hangs in the garage. It must then be emptied and replaced carefully. On Sunday the total rainfall for the week has to be entered into the logbook which is kept in the top drawer in the kitchen.'

'Well that all sounds fairly straightforward but why does he do it?'

'I have absolutely no idea.'

'Well at least it's not too taxing.'

'I haven't finished yet. Next is the electricity reading for the solar panels, both input and output. It's something to do with being paid for any energy that gets fed back into the national grid. The figures need to be recorded in the blue book which hangs next to the clipboard. Then, of course, we need to monitor the temperature on the fish-tank which should remain at a steady 25 to 27 degrees. Any huge deviation and the fish could die, oh and one of them's pregnant, so we need to keep an eye out in case the other fish eat the eggs. They need to have a sachet of frozen food which has to be defrosted and rinsed in a sieve before being put in the tank. Meanwhile Heidi needs to have a cupful of kibble morning and evening, once at 7am and the other at 7pm. When she goes out she has to wear her boots to protect her paws and her coat to keep her fur dry, especially with the show coming up. The orchids should be left alone but the other plants need watering once a week but there's a measure in the utility room for doing that.'

'Good grief. Have you finished or is there more?'

'Just the security system and the heating but I can show you that tomorrow.'

'Heavens, I'm exhausted just listening to it all. You've got your work cut out then Mr Baird!'

'What do you mean, *I've* got my work cut out? Those are shared responsibilities and you know I'm no good at technical things Chris. You'll have to help.'

'I'll think about it in the morning. *Gute Nacht mein Schatz.*'

After having waved goodbye to our hosts the following morning and given Heidi her breakfast we realise that we'd better get her out for her morning walk. It turns out that putting on our walking boots is a great deal easier than trying to put four boots on a poodle. Heidi clearly doesn't like the idea in spite of what we were told, and makes our task doubly awkward with her wild protest.

Having donned her coat and set the security system, we head off to the forest which borders the small estate. However, no sooner are we out of the door than we stand back in amazement as she trots along on her lead beside Rob looking more like a horse in a dressage competition. At each step she lifts her legs high off the ground as if she's walking on hot coals that are burning her paws.

'Good grief! Do you think we've put her boots on the wrong way?' puzzles Rob, watching as Heidi continues to prance along the road.

'I've no idea darling. It's quite bizarre. That's a good point though. Maybe we have.'

After a few adjustments we set off again but no, Heidi is still dancing along like a Lipizzaner, her head held high at a haughty angle.

'This is excruciatingly embarrassing Chris. Do you think

this is how she normally walks? I feel a right idiot. Here, you take her.'

'Why should I take her? You were the one who wanted to take the lead. Anyhow, I think I need to get this on video.'

'You dare! If it ends up on Twitter this could lead to divorce,' says Rob, scowling at me. 'I'm going to go round the block and then I'm taking her in.'

So while we sit over a welcome cup of coffee, poor Heidi is lying in her bed, chin on paws, looking pleadingly in my direction.

'Don't look at me like that, it was cruel Uncle Rob who brought you home,' I say, trying not to laugh. 'But seriously Rob, we have to take her for decent walks, she needs the exercise and after all, it's what we're here for.'

'Well you can take her out, or if I do it's going to be after nightfall. I felt like the laughing stock of the neighbourhood.'

'Maybe it's to do with being in the show ring? A lot of the dogs move in a rather exaggerated way.'

'Yes, and the owners,' replies Rob, 'but no way am I going to make an exhibition of myself.'

Rob proves to be really serious about refusing to walk poor Heidi so each day I set off, having kitted the pair of us out, for a good trot round the forest paths. It's beautiful to see the snow untouched by any footprints but quite hazardous in some areas where it's been compacted and turned into an icy skid-path. Heidi's boots prove more efficient than mine, especially when I attempt my best Crufts show-walk, with Heidi's lead held high and her running with extended legs. We get some bemused looks from other walkers, especially those with common or garden dogs, but she's actually quite beautiful in action.

Every day, on returning to the house, I set about grooming her, trying to recall the tutorial that Elsbeth gave me. I lay out the various brushes and combs and painstakingly tease out any small knots in her coat before brushing her, trying hard not to scratch her skin. She's very laid back about the whole business and extremely cooperative but as her coat is getting quite long it's no easy job. Her long, bare muzzle gives way to a huge, furry pom-pom which has to be held back in two rubber bands and the huge ruff around her neck proves quite a challenge. I'm nervous of hurting her but she doesn't seem to be overly bothered.

It's one morning, having returned to the house and started to brush her, that Rob comes wandering in to observe.

'Good grief. What a palaver. Fancy having to go through this ritual every day.'

'Well apparently the fur can get matted very easily so it has to be done. It'll make the groomer's job easier when she comes.'

'But why do they have to have such ridiculous hair-dos?'

'According to Elsbeth they were once used for hunting and if they went into water their coat became very heavy, so a lot of it was cut back, but in order to keep their essential bits warm, they let the fur in those areas grow.'

'My, you have been doing your homework. That's actually very interesting and explains a lot. But it's this over-the-top pampering that I can't cope with. Some of them really do look ridiculous.'

'To change the subject darling, have you remembered to do your readings today? There was quite a lot of rain last night.'

'That's a point, I'd better go and do my duties. Still no sign of the fish eggs by the way, but I've checked the temperature and it's fine.'

It's only when he turns round that I notice that Rob is wearing a pair of jeans that I don't recognise.

'Are those new?' I ask, waiting for the creative explanation as to why my beloved needed to buy yet more clothes.

'Yes, reduced in the M&S sale, what do you think?' he replies, giving me a twirl.

'Very nice, but for heaven's sake, don't go sitting on the white settee until they've been through the wash. New denim's terrible for marking things. In fact if you pop them off now and leave them on the floor in the utility room I'll give them a quick wash this evening.'

As darkness falls, just as I'm about to put my kit on to take Heidi out, a hesitant voice calls through from the kitchen.

'I'll take her Chris,' offers my husband gallantly. 'It's about time I did my share and at least no-one will see us.'

'Oh thank you. I'd really appreciate it and then I can get on with dinner. You only need to go round the block. But don't stay out long, it's bitterly cold and it's supposed to snow again this evening.'

It's about twenty minutes later when Rob returns with a dusting of snow on his hat.

'Gosh, it's cold out there! I didn't think we should stay outside any longer. Anyhow, she's had a good walk, or should I say prance? Those boots are actually quite effective. She manages to walk quite briskly doesn't she?'

'Yes, they do seem to help,' I reply. 'If you give me her coat I'll hang it up in the utility room to dry.'

'Oh crikey. I'm sorry Chris. I didn't put it on her. It was such a palaver getting her boots on that I totally forgot about it.'

'Well I hope her fur hasn't got too wet. I'd better go and get her dried or her coat'll get matted and you'll have undone all my hard work. Anyhow, where is she?'

'I left her in the utility room so that she could dry off a bit. I didn't think you'd want her in here.'

'Too right I don't! I'd better go and see what she's up to.'

Surprisingly Heidi isn't up to anything, but has already made herself comfy on the floor as the underfloor heating makes the tiles nice and warm.

'Here Heidi, let's get you dry,' I say encouragingly.

She dutifully gets up but, on beginning to pat her dry with a towel, I notice to my alarm that one side of her has turned a delicate shade of blue. I realise immediately what's happened. Our precious show-dog, who is due in the ring in five days, has been dyed a fetching shade of denim blue.

'Rob!' I scream. 'Rob! I need you.'

'Are you alright darling?' he asks, rushing through from the kitchen.

'Well I am but Heidi isn't. Look!'

'Oh crikey! How on earth has that happened?'

'Well it's pretty obvious, isn't it? She came in wet and has lain down on your new jeans. How we're going to deal with this I don't know.'

'Can't we give her a bath?'

'No, of course we can't. That'll only make the colour transfer to the rest of her coat.'

'How's about a trim then?'

'Rob, grooming poodles is a highly skilled job. It's not something we can do. She's a big enough mess without us attacking her with a pair of shears.'

'Well the doggy hairdresser comes tomorrow, hopefully she can do something.'

'We've just got to hope it hasn't got to her undercoat or we really are in trouble. I'll give her a gentle blow-dry and then she'll to have to stay in here for the night, and for heaven's sake don't let her near the white settee.'

It's the following afternoon when the *Hundecoiffeurei* van turns into the drive and a stunningly beautiful blonde, probably in her late twenties, climbs down from the driver's cab, her skinny jeans and tight sweater leaving little to the imagination. When the doorbell rings Rob hurries eagerly to the door to welcome her while I go to get Heidi. As I lead our charge out to the garden I can't help but recognise the broad smile and besotted expression on Rob's face.

'*Guten Morgen.* Well here she is,' I say as I hand Heidi over to the young woman. 'I'm afraid we had an accident. I do hope you can help,' I add, pointing to the large blue patch on Heidi's side.

'*Oh mein Gott. Sie ist ganz blau geworden!*' she laughs, covering her face with her hands in horror. 'Yes, I think it will be okay because here I am cutting the hair to her skin,' she replies, running her hand along Heidi's back.

'Oh, what a relief!' says Rob. 'And I'm sorry, I didn't ask your name.'

'I'm Heidi,' she announces, blushing. 'You have two of us!'

'And both of you very pretty,' says Rob, his eyes twinkling.

'Well, if you are liking to leave her with me, I will start. She must be very beautiful because of the show,' says Heidi, sounding business-like.

'How long will it take?' I ask.

'About one hour and a half,' she replies. 'I will call when she is finished.'

And so Rob and I return to the house to while away the time.

'I've been meaning to tell you Rob, I came across some interesting facts on the internet about Switzerland. Some of them are unbelievable.'

'Such as?' asks Rob.

'Well, you're not allowed to mow the lawn, hang out your washing or do the recycling on a Sunday.'

'Nothing wrong with that, it sounds eminently sensible to me.'

'And if you live in an apartment you shouldn't flush the loo after ten o'clock at night and you fellas are supposed to pee sitting down.'

'Good grief, that's going a bit far isn't it?'

'And this is the best one, it's against the law to keep a guinea pig, a parrot, a budgie or a goldfish on its own.'

'Against the law? You mean you can be fined or go to prison for having one guinea pig? What if you have two and one snuffs it?'

'Well I guess you go and find it a friend sharpish. But here, let me read you this, I say, reaching for my iPad. "Dog-owners have to go on a course that teaches them how to look after their dog, care for its needs and deal with a range of behavioural issues." I reckon that's a brilliant bit of legislation. It's a pity more countries don't adopt the ruling.'

At that moment the cuckoo emerges from the depths of the clock and makes us jump.

'It's a pity they haven't insisted that all cuckoo clocks should be silenced after nine o'clock at night,' moans Rob. 'That damned thing wakes me up every evening, just after I've managed to get off to sleep. Actually, looking at the time, I think I'll just go and see how Heidi's getting on.'

'And which of the two Heidis are you referring to I wonder?'

'The one with the blue eyes,' he replies provocatively and goes to investigate.

It's some twenty minutes later that I think I'd better go and check on progress. I climb up the steps of the van and open the door to be greeted by something akin to an alien. Heidi (the canine form) has been transformed into a series of large, white clouds and the bits in between shorn back to her skin. She looks like a piece of doggy topiary. Even I'm shocked by the metamorphosis. Rob is looking aghast at the apparition before him.

'Well, what do you think of our lady?' asks Heidi. 'Is she not beautiful?'

'She certainly is,' I reply, still looking in awe at the strange creature that has emerged from the grooming session and wondering how on earth we're going to keep her in such pristine condition before Theo and Elsbeth return the following afternoon.

We sit watching the cuckoo-clock, awaiting their arrival.

'Now are all the record books up to date?' I ask Rob, suddenly panicking that we might have neglected some of our duties.

'Yes, I've entered all the figures so everything's in order but still no sign of the fish laying any eggs. She still looks a bit bloated so either she's still pregnant or she's eaten them,' he replies.

Having been too afraid to get Heidi dirty or dishevelled after her time with Heidi number two (which, I discovered cost a mere €115) we confine her to the house and garden so that, when her doting owners return, they're delighted with her appearance. As they arrive at the gate Heidi's tail, which now looks somewhat like an exotic bottle-brush, is wagging furiously and she leaps up excitedly to greet Theo as he walks up the path.

'Oh, my lovely, you are looking so beautiful,' he says, giving her a huge hug. 'Rob and Christine have made a wonderful job of looking after you.'

'Really, we can't thank you enough,' says Elsbeth, almost tearful with gratitude. 'She looks so glamorous. She's in tip-top condition. Let's hope we do well at the show.'

'You must let us know how she gets on,' I reply. 'We'll be keeping everything crossed for her.'

Two days later, having left the majesty of Switzerland behind and finding ourselves at Gatwick Airport awaiting our return flight to the island, I'm a little anxious when my phone shows that I have a message from Elsbeth. However, my anxiety quickly disappears when I see that it's a photo of a rather splendid-looking Heidi next to a red rosette and a large silver trophy. I can't help but well up with pride, especially when I see the look of absolute joy on Elsbeth and Theo's faces.

'Oh quick Rob, come and see! It's a photo of Heidi!'

My man drops his newspaper immediately and is soon peering over my shoulder to get a good look at the picture.

'Look! She won! She came first in class. Isn't that wonderful? They must be thrilled.'

'For a moment I thought you meant the glamorous one,' replies Rob with a hint of disappointment.

'This is the glamorous one Mr Baird. "Let's enjoy the beautiful things we can see, my dear, and not think about those we cannot."'

'Crikey, that's a bit poetic. Did you just make that up?'

'No, it's actually a quote from one of my favourite childhood books.'

'Oh, and which one was that?'

'Heidi,' I reply, heading off to the duty-free shop.

EDINBURGH ROCKS

'I'm bored,' comes a voice from the sitting-room.

As I peer through from the kitchen I can only see Rob's back, shoulders slumped, where he's standing gazing out of the window, hands in pockets.

'Well why not go and mow the lawn? It could do with a good cut, it's full of dandelions and it's beginning to look pretty shabby,' I respond, heading towards the table with two mugs of tea.

'I'll have you know that that's my new pollinator patch and anyhow it's still too wet. The grass'll clog up the mower,' he replies, wandering into the kitchen and flopping into his chair. 'Couldn't you find us another house-sit Chris? I could do with a change of scenery and I miss not having a furry friend. Do you know the house still feels empty without our two and it must be what, three years since we had to say goodbye to Holly?'

'I know love, I still miss them too, but I have to confess that I do enjoy the freedom now that we're on our own. Those late-night walks in the rain weren't too much fun.'

'No, I suppose you're right. It was a bit of a pain getting kitted out at eleven o'clock at night when all you wanted to do was crawl into bed. So what do you reckon? Is there anything interesting on the web-site?'

'I don't know, I must admit I haven't looked for a while. If you pass the lap-top we can have a search. Where do you fancy going before I waste my energy looking at places you don't want to go?'

'What's that supposed to mean? I'll go anywhere.'

'No you won't, we've been through this before, there are lots of places you refuse to even consider.'

'Okay, try me.'

'Australia.'

'Oh come on Chris, you know I think that's too far. I've said before, I don't want to do any long-haul flights.'

'There you are then, you won't go anywhere. You don't like foreign food, you don't like not being able to speak the language and you hate hanging around in airports. We may as well stay at home.'

'Oh that's unfair. But yes, you're right, I am tired of airports but we don't have much choice if we want to get off the island.'

'Precisely. So if we can't face Gatwick you have a choice; Bristol, Manchester, Birmingham, Southampton …'

'No, don't fancy any of those. English cities don't do it for me unless it's Bath or York.'

'Well what about Edinburgh? We haven't been there since your parents died.'

'That's true. It might be nice to go home for a trip down memory lane. Let's have a look.'

I'm quietly surprised when, after entering Edinburgh in the search, three sits come up. I click on the first one which shows a picture of a three-story granite house.

'So what does the blurb say?' asks Rob.

'"We have three energetic, boisterous young dogs who are like no others I've ever owned or met. They're going to need adult only sitters who are not afraid of reactive behaviour and can spend time getting to know them."'

'Well you needn't even consider putting that one on the list. There is no way I'm going to be dragged round Edinburgh by three dogs that haven't been socialised. I'm surprised they've got the nerve to advertise for sitters. How about the second one?' asks Rob, peering at the screen. '"Enjoy the Athens of the north in the company of two delightful Airedales."'

'Airedales are big dogs Rob. What do they say about them?'

'"Digby takes medication twice a day for arthritis and needs to attend hydrotherapy twice a week. He can no longer manage long walks but loves to get out for a couple of hours each day. He can manage six to seven miles but would need to rest the following day."'

'Crikey, so would I. That's quite a hike.'

'There's more. "Bella needs to be reminded who's in charge. She's a bit of a princess and hates the hoover."'

'That's all spelling hard work Rob. Scroll down to the last one, let's see. "Angus and Maggie are two border terriers …"'

'Done!' cries Rob with a big smile on his face.

'Just because they're borders doesn't mean it's a suitable sit Rob, just hang on a minute and let's read the rest of it. "Our home is in Corstorphine on the edge of a golf course and very close to Edinburgh Zoo." Oh that sounds wonderful, we could go and see the pandas! "Angus is diabetic and needs twice daily injections at 7am and 7pm. Maggie is now seventeen and is suffering from dementia. She sometimes refuses to eat and will need encouraging." This sounds like a carbon copy of our two Rob. I know diabetes is a big responsibility but what do you reckon?'

'Well as you say, it isn't as though we haven't been through diabetes and dementia already. It must be difficult for the owners to get sitters who know how to care for a diabetic dog and administer insulin. I'd be happy to give it a go and I could show you some of my old stomping ground. As you say, it's a good while since we were up there. Why not? Let's apply and see what happens.'

We're delighted to get an almost instant reply from the owners, Andrew and Shona, who, as we had guessed, had been having difficulty finding sitters due to the dogs' health.

'They seem delighted darling. I've just had a chat with Shona and told her about our two. She seemed reassured that we were up for it. So, I suppose I'd better get the flights booked.'

'Well it'll be a delight not to have spend time at Gatwick

that's for sure,' muses Rob, 'and we can get straight into Waverley station from the airport and then a bus up to Corstorphine. Oh it's good to have something to look forward to again.'

'Well you'd better get packing Mr Baird, you've only got six days to organise your wardrobe, what are you waiting for?'

The doggy radar has already picked up on our arrival when we ring the front doorbell. As the door opens the two dogs run out into the drive barking madly. These two could easily be a reincarnation of our own borders, Rufus and Holly. They're one breed where there's a definite difference between the sexes, the females tending to look more feminine and pretty while the males look more feisty and ready for action. Maggie is indeed pretty despite her advanced years and Angus has the stocky stance of the breed with a head akin to an otter.

'Hello there, you're a handsome pair,' says Rob, bending down to greet our new charges. 'And I do apologise, you must be Shona,' he says, getting back up onto his feet and holding out his hand in greeting to our hostess. 'I'm sorry, that was most rude of me, but I have a bad habit of greeting the dog before the owner! How do you do, it's nice to meet you at last.'

'And you,' replies Shona, taking Rob's hand and wrapping it in hers. 'Do come in. And Christine,' she says turning to me with a warm smile. 'Oh this is so wonderful, I can't begin to tell you what a joy it's been to find you two.' She's the sort of woman it's difficult to age. Her greying hair is held back with a pair of tortoiseshell combs, her skin showing the inevitable wrinkles that come with old age, but she could be an elderly-looking sixty or a young eighty, there's no way of telling. 'And do I hear a hint of an Edinburgh accent there Rob?' she asks.

'Yes, born and bred but I've been away from home for a long time now. And yourself?'

'Well, I'm Edinburgh but Andrew's from Orkney. He'll be with us in a moment, he's just packing the car. It's a man's job according to him,' she laughs. 'Do come through and sit yourselves down and I'll put the kettle on.'

'So are you going far?' I ask, noticing the luggage piled in the doorway.

'No, we don't stray too far these days because of the dogs. We like to be close at hand in case of an emergency. We're just going to play a few rounds of golf along the east coast finishing with an overnight at St Andrew's. As you know it's only for a week but it'll be good to have a break. Dear Angus's diabetes does clobber our social life but I'm sure you know all about that! Ah, here comes Andrew.'

A decidedly elderly man with stooped shoulders emerges from the garage. He's virtually bald and has a kind face with somewhat protruding eyes. On seeing us both he smiles warmly and stretches out his arm to shake hands.

'I canna for the life of me remember yer names but welcome. Shona's probably told you all about me. I'm the trouble-maker roond here,' he laughs. 'Anyhow, come on through to the lounge before these two bark the hoos doon.'

We're led into the sitting-room which is decorated in a soft green and smartly furnished with a plush three-piece suite. An antique, glass-topped coffee table sits in the centre of a vast Chinese carpet and a row of ornamental dancers lines the mantlepiece above the stone fireplace. One wall of the room is taken up with the biggest television screen I have ever seen in someone's house. Shona must have noticed me looking at it.

'That beast is Andrew's pride and joy Christine. He really enjoys the television, especially as we can't get out very much these days.'

Not having a television ourselves I'm already hoping that the instructions have been included in our housesitters' guide or we'll be looking at a blank screen for seven days. We're suddenly joined by the dogs who do several circuits of the coffee table before disappearing out of the door barking furiously and then returning for another round of the furniture. Andrew puts his hands over his ears and rolls his eyes.

'You'll be familiar with all this nonsense having had borders yersels!' he laughs, trying to make himself heard above the noise. The barking is abated by a firm order for them to go to their baskets, which they surprisingly do.

'Well hopefully that'll give us two minutes peace,' smiles Shona returning with a tray of pretty tea-cups. 'We need to talk you through the routine but it's all in the notes and if you have any concerns then do please ring us. It's such a relief for us to find someone who's familiar with diabetes, it tends to put sitters off applying but that's understandable isn't it? I'm afraid it does tie you down as you well know. Gone are the days of going to the theatre as everything tends to start at 7.30.'

'Yes, that pleasure has been denied us I'm afraid,' interrupts Andrew. 'The boy has to have his jag at 7.00 in the morning and again at 7.00 in the evening after he's eaten and you'll need to keep an eye on him for half an hour afterwards just in case he goes wobbly, but he's very good, he'll even come and look for you if you're not punctual. It's as though he knows he needs it.'

'His insulin is in the fridge,' continues Shona looking almost apologetic, 'it's in the door and clearly labelled and there's a bucket on the back of the door for the used needles. Their food is in the utility room but, as you'll be aware, Angus has to have a strict diet, no treats or scraps, so I tend to feed them separately otherwise you have to stand over them to make sure he doesn't steal Maggie's food.'

'And don't be fooled by her sweet expression, she's a wee stunner but she's not the brightest bless her,' chuckles Andrew.

'I'm afraid doggy dementia is setting in, and sometimes she forgets how to eat or drink. I find that just getting a small amount in her mouth helps to trigger her memory,' says Shona, her eyes welling up. 'Oh dear, I'm so sorry, it's only when I explain it all to someone that I realise how much care they need. We're so lucky to have found you both. We can't thank you enough.'

'Don't you worry Shona,' says Rob reassuringly. 'We've been there ourselves and I'm sure we'll all manage and, as you say, you're at the end of a phone and not too far away if we need you for any reason.'

'And before we go,' says Andrew, 'there's a wee bottle of whisky for you on the sideboard. It's an Orkney special from Scapa. Please help yerself!'

'That's very generous of you Andrew but quite unnecessary. Thank you so much, I'm sure we'll enjoy it!' replies Rob.

It's two days into our stay and everything is going well. We've established a routine and the dogs seem quite happy with their new staff. Angus behaves really well when he has to have his injection and Maggie manages to eat well with a little encouragement.

'They're absolute sweethearts aren't they?' remarks Rob while we're eating breakfast. 'I can't say I enjoy the early start to the day but Angus is such a warrior. You can feel how his neck has toughened up with all the injections poor lad. It can't be much fun.'

'You're so good with him though Rob. I must admit that I've become a bit less confident with a syringe. It seems such a long time since we had to inject poor old Rufus.'

'Well it must be eight years now. But do you know I still miss him Chris?'

'Oh don't start me off,' I reply, already choking on my words. 'So what are we going to do with our day? You told me you had something to show me.'

'I have indeed, but it'll have to wait until we've given these two a good walk as we'll need to get the bus into town.'

'Oh, I didn't realise it was in town. So where are we heading?'

'You'll have to wait and see,' replies my man with a wicked twinkle in his eyes.

It's later that afternoon that I find myself standing in a dark, narrow street lined on either side by austere, granite buildings, some of them so high that they stop any light from entering the dim corridor. A line of wheelie bins next to the back door of one of them suggests that it's accommodation of sorts. There's a dank smell coming from the drains and it's an altogether unsavoury place.

'If it isn't a silly question darling, why have you brought me here? I assume it's because of some historical interest that's usually omitted from the standard tourist itinerary?'

'This building happens to be of huge historic interest,' replies Rob with a flourish. 'This Chris, is the back of the Drumond Hotel where your beloved husband worked when he was a young man.'

'Well that's interesting sweetheart but why have you brought me to the back door?'

'Come and stand over here,' says Rob, taking my hand and pulling me back against the wall opposite the bins. 'Now look up. You see that window just below the parapet around the roof, let's see,' he mutters, quietly counting the floors, 'the one on the seventh floor, second from the end?'

I count carefully as this is clearly important to my man, 'Yes, I've got it. Why was that your room?'

'Yes, it was staff accommodation. I lived up there for eighteen months in 1968.'

'Fascinating darling. I'm so pleased you showed it to me. It's lovely to see places that were special to you. So can we go now? I'd like to do a bit of shopping on Princes Street if you don't mind?'

'But I haven't told you the story yet,' replies Rob, clearly disappointed that I'm not showing any enthusiasm.

'You mean there's more?'

'I haven't even started.'

'Well come on then, let's hear it. You got set upon by a gang one night outside the back door?'

'No, it's much more terrifying than that. I was in charge of opening up the Tartan Bar ready for the evening and, to my horror, one afternoon I got shut out of my room and the keys to the bar were in my bedroom in my jacket pocket. I was too afraid to tell anyone in case I got into trouble so I decided that the only thing to do was to retrieve the keys.'

'I assume somebody had a spare set?'

'Well probably, but as I said I was too worried that I'd be in trouble. I decided that the only way to get into my room was to access it from the adjoining room which was also staff accommodation.'

'So you mean there was an adjoining door?'

'No unfortunately, the only way was to go into the next room and climb out onto the window-ledge.'

I can't help but utter a sharp cry when I realise where this story is heading. 'Oh my God Rob, but you can't stand heights! I can't bear to think about it. So you mean you climbed from that window-sill onto yours?'

'Yes. And no, I have no idea how I did it. I had to get from that window-sill,' he says pointing up, 'to that window-sill and then open the window and climb in.'

I'm feeling decidedly ill at the very thought. 'But darling you could have died. What if you'd fallen?'

'I know and I still don't know to this day how I did it.'

'I think I need a stiff drink Rob. That's really upset me.' I can literally feel my legs shaking and am trying to rid my imagination of my husband clinging on to a granite wall, James Bond style, and stepping across the sizeable gap between the two rooms. I grab hold of him for comfort, my eyes welling up.

'I think you're right sweetheart, let's go and have a wee dram and then we must get back to the dogs or there'll be puddles on the floor.'

'Yes, and I've got a chicken to cook for dinner so we'd better not be too late getting home.'

Fortunately there are no puddles but there are two very excited dogs. Maggie waddles off to her basket and returns with her favourite toy for Rob while Angus tears out into the garden to water a few shrubs.

'Oh it is lovely to come home to a couple of waggy tails Chris. It makes me think we should reconsider our decision not to …'

'No!' I say firmly. 'We've had this discussion a thousand times Rob. We're not having another dog and that's that.'

'Well that's me told Angus,' says Rob in a pitiful voice as Angus returns, bending down to ruffle his ears. 'Come on, let's get you out for a quick walk while Aunty Christine cooks dinner. I'll leave Mags with you darling, she's happy enough having a wander round the garden. I reckon she's got a touch of arthritis in that back leg. I'll just take his nibs along the path by the golf course. Won't be long.'

'Alright. Dinner should be ready about seven. And don't get lost!' I shout as man and dog disappear down the path.

It's almost an hour later when Rob returns with Angus whose nose is coated with wet sand. I fear the worst.

'I didn't realise there was a beach close by, so where have you two intrepid travellers been might I ask?'

'Er, the golf course,' replies Rob, 'as intended.'

'And dare I ask which part of the golf course? Could it by any chance have involved a bunker?'

Rob looks suitably sheepish. 'No,' he replies, 'just a newly seeded area of the fairway. All the golfers had gone home so I decided to let him off the lead. He headed straight for an area near to the fourteenth hole and started to dig for England.'

'You mean Scotland,' I correct.

'Oh alright if you must be pedantic. Anyhow, I don't think anyone saw him so you needn't get upset. There's just a rather large hole near to the green.'

'Oh honestly Rob. You're hopeless. If he'd been caught we'd

be facing a huge bill for the damage. Maybe it would be better if you walked him on the path by the zoo in future. He can't possibly get through the fencing.'

'Oh alright if you insist. Anyhow, something smells good, is dinner ready yet?'

'Ten minutes, but you'd better give them both their grub and then inject Angus. If you sort them out I can get everything served up.'

Half an hour later we take our wine to the sitting room and fall into an armchair each. The dogs join us, Angus lying at Rob's feet and Maggie standing staring at a wall.

'Oh bless her. She really is losing her marbles Chris. Look at her. She'll still be like that in half an hour unless I move her. Here Mags,' he says, crossing the room and scooping her up in his arms. 'Come and sit on my knee for a while.' The pair of them snuggle down in Rob's chair, Maggie with her head on his shoulder. 'So what did you make of my Spiderman exploits? Who said I wasn't one for adventure?'

'To be honest I'm still in awe darling. I cannot for the life of me imagine you up there. I'm probably going to have a nightmare tonight.'

'Speaking of nightmares, the chicken this evening reminded me of another horror story from that hotel.'

'A chicken? How can a chicken be the subject of a horror story?' I ask, taking a sip from my glass.

'Well on Sunday evenings we used to put on light bar snacks for coach parties. We'd get a whole crowd in so it had to be something we could produce quickly, needless to say, chicken sandwiches were a regular standby.'

'I can't imagine where this story's going but go on,' I say, curling up in my armchair.

'We used to serve roast chicken for Sunday lunch and then use up the left-overs for sandwiches. As we couldn't put a warm carcass in the fridge we were instructed to cover it with a damp t-towel to keep the meat moist.'

'Yuk. That doesn't sound very hygienic. So it was sitting around in the kitchen from lunch-time until your coach party arrived for tea?'

'Exactly. Well one afternoon we'd all had an hour or so off after lunch and went back to work for the afternoon shift. I unlocked the bar and went through the swing doors into the kitchen only to see the t-towel on the top of the chicken moving.'

'Moving? Oh my God what was it?' I ask, sitting up and awaiting the horror that I've been prepared for.

'Mice. Lots of them. The carcass was alive with them.'

'Oh Rob, that's utterly disgusting. I feel sick just thinking about it. I trust you binned it, but I guess chicken sandwiches were off the menu that day?'

'Oh no, we served it up,' he says laughing.

'I don't believe you. You're having me on. You couldn't possibly do that,' I say leaning forward and looking at him intently.

'I assure you we did.'

'But the customers would have been seriously ill and your reputation ruined.'

'You have to remember there was no social media in 1968. No Trip Advisor or a chance to leave feedback. The holiday company would have had difficulty proving it was us.'

'Oh that's gross. I don't think I'll ever be able to look at a chicken carcass again without thinking of that story. Speaking of which, where did Angus go? I saw him get up just a moment ago. I hope to goodness he hasn't snaffled the chicken,' and at that I leap up and run into the kitchen. 'Just in time!' I shout through to the sitting-room. 'His nibs was just about to help himself. It's rotten that he can't have even a tiny bit of chicken. I feel so mean when he looks at me with those big, sad eyes. Anyhow, looking at the time we'd better get these two round the block.'

We don our jackets and wander down the road, keeping to the footpath alongside the boundary to the zoo. There's a high, stone wall for most of the way so we can't actually see into the park although we can hear some of the animals howling and barking.

'These two don't seem at all bothered by the noise do they?' remarks Rob trying to peer over the wall.

'I suppose they're used to it after all these years. I do hope we're going to get to see the pandas before we leave, they're on my bucket list.'

'In which case we'll definitely have to arrange a visit. They used to have a wonderful collection of animals when I was living here. Did I ever tell you about the lion?'

'No, what lion?' I ask, stopping to let Maggie have a sniff around a bush.

'It was probably in the 70s after I'd left, but apparently they rescued a lion that was being used as part of a striptease act.'

'Oh Rob, now you really are having me on.'

'I promise you I'm not, you can check when we get home if you don't believe me.'

'I'm beginning to wonder if that story about the chicken was true. The trouble with you is you're always telling porkies. It's hardly surprising people find it hard to believe you. Anyhow, I can't imagine anyone in their right senses wanting to take their clothes off anywhere near a creature with huge teeth and six inch claws.'

'Well clearly one woman did.'

We eventually get back to the house and Rob reaches for his iPad.

'Here, I told you it was true,' he says triumphantly. '"An inspector was called to a house in the city where a lion had been spotted. It belonged to an exotic dancer who used to perform with the animal in bars. On entering the house he discovered a half-grown lioness in the back garden being fed on dozens of tins of cat food and huge pans of milk by its owner who was a go-go dancer."'

'That's awful Rob. There really are some sick people around. Anyhow, I'm going to head for bed. Do you want a whisky before I go up?'

'Now there's a good idea. Yes please my darling wife, I'd love one. But no water thanks.'

I pour a measure of the Scapa into a tumbler and pop it on the table next to Rob before heading for bed. 'Don't be too late and make sure you shut the kitchen door so that the dogs can't get into the sitting-room. Night night.'

'Night darling. Sleep tight.'

It's the following morning that I'm woken by a noise coming from outside our bedroom door. It seems to be quite a commotion. The door is pushed open and in walks Maggie looking lost. I turn to Rob and shake him by the shoulder.

'What's going on?' asks a sleepy voice from under the duvet.

'Dare I ask if you remembered to close the kitchen door last night when you came to bed?'

'Er, I think maybe I forgot. It was rather late and I was pretty tired, why?'

'Because Maggie's just turned up and there's an awful kerfuffle coming from the landing. I think I'd better go and investigate.'

To my horror, on opening the door, there are clumps of what appears to be black fur all over the carpet and Angus has got something clasped firmly in his jaws which he's shaking manically. I can't for the life of me work out what it is.

'Rob, I need you,' I shout. 'Angus has got something.'

'What on earth's going on out here?' asks Rob, appearing bleary-eyed in his pyjamas.

'He's got something in his mouth but I can't work out what it is. Here Angus, drop it!' I say firmly, approaching him slowly and ready to grab the offending article, but he dashes downstairs and disappears into the sitting-room. 'Oh this is fun,' I call back up the stairs as I run down in hot pursuit.

'Mind he doesn't bite you!' shouts Rob.

'Oh thanks a million, there's nothing like coming to help me,' I call back.

As I enter the sitting-room Angus clearly works out my intentions and scoots off round the coffee table making several circuits at high speed before escaping through the door into the kitchen. He clearly thinks this is a good game. I quickly run after him and shut the kitchen door behind me. Trapped!

'Here Angus, drop it! Come on, give!' I command, moving slowly closer to him. I'm met by a deep growl. I decide that making out I'm going to feed him is the answer and the moment my hand stretches out towards the door of the pantry he's by my side, abandoning his spoils on the floor. I quickly bend down and scoop the thing off the floor only to be met by manic barking. He is not a happy dog. Rob, clearly wondering what on earth is going on sticks his head round the door.

'Is everything alright in here? What on earth has got him so wound up?' he shouts.

'Here, take this,' I say passing the somewhat chewed article round the door and removing another clump of black fur from the front of my dressing-gown. 'I'm going to leave him in here to calm down.' And with that I squeeze round the side of the door pulling it firmly behind me. The barking continues.

'So what on earth has he got? It looks revolting,' I say looking at what appears to be a piece of soggy leather with bits of fur stuck to it.

'I hate to say it but I think it's a sporran, or rather what's left of one.'

'A sporran? But where on earth could he have got it from?'

'I guess he got into Andrew and Shona's bedroom. Oh crikey, this is a real mess Chris.'

'Well we're clearly going to have to get it repaired and sharpish. They'll be back on Sunday. Andrew'll be furious.'

'There might be somebody local who can sort it, after all we are in Edinburgh. I know there are companies who make kilts so hopefully they do sporrans as well.'

As Rob starts a search I examine the remains of Angus's quarry. Apart from a couple of teeth marks in the leather it's mainly the fur that's been pulled out. As I consider the damage, Angus emerges from the kitchen and, seeing me with his trophy, starts growling.

'No you can't have it Angus. You're a bad dog do you hear me? A bad dog.' Angus gives me a bemused look and a cute head tilt. 'And it's no use trying the cute look either. This is going to cost money. That's your treats gone for the next week.' It's then that I remind myself that poor Angus doesn't get any treats and now I feel bad. 'Go on, go to your basket.' His tail goes down and as he heads for his basket he looks mournfully back at me.

'You do realise that Maggie's probably just as guilty Chris,' suggests Rob. Just because she's not the brightest bulb in the box it doesn't mean she wasn't his partner in crime.'

'That's very true. So she'd better go in her basket as well. Speaking of Mags, where is she?'

'No idea,' replies Rob continuing his search for a sporran repairer.

I trace my steps back to the sitting-room where I find Maggie staring at a wall. 'Oh bless you, come on Maggie. It seems you have to serve your time too,' I say, picking her up in my arms and carrying her back to the kitchen. Angus is lying with his head hanging over the edge of his basket sulking, although his tail is drumming against the wall and, as I place Mags in hers, he heaves a great sigh. 'You know I love you really but you're not very popular at the moment,' I say looking down at him and giving him what I hope is a severe look.

'Got it!' cries Rob. 'There's a place called Scott's not far from here. They're closed until ten o'clock but I'll drop them an email and see if they can help.'

Fortunately the lovely people at Scott's are only too pleased to help and appreciate our dilemma, so the next afternoon, with Andrew's sporran carefully packed into a bag, Rob sets off to find the shop.

'You won't get lost now will you?' I call as he heads off down the drive.

'I lived here for over twenty years Chris, I think I can find my way without any trouble but thanks for your concern. I'll see you later.'

It wouldn't be the first time Rob had got lost. I don't think I've ever met anyone with a worse sense of direction. He admits himself that he could get lost in a telephone box. I recall sending a friend an email when we were on holiday in Italy saying that he'd gone out to buy wine and that I was worried I might never see him again. The reply came back, '*Oh no? Has he got dementia?*' I replied, '*No, just a lousy sense of direction.*'

It's a good four hours later and there's still no sign of him so I ring his phone. Needless to say it's switched off. I can only assume that the repair is taking a little longer than anticipated. Maybe they're trying to find a rogue black rabbit or the work is more skilled than we'd thought. With no way of contacting him I realise I'm just going to have to sit this one out and hope that he isn't wandering the back streets of Edinburgh trying to find his way back to Corstorphine. As seven o'clock approaches I realise I'm going to have to feed the dogs and inject Angus. I put the food down for them and head for the fridge and the insulin when suddenly the back door opens with a flourish and a somewhat florid-faced husband appears.

'I love a lassie, a bonny, bonny lassie, she's as pure as the lily in the dell,' sings a somewhat discordant voice coming from the hallway. 'Hello my darling wife.'

'Thank goodness you're home, I was getting worried about you. You've been ages.'

'Well give this husband of yours a wee kiss,' he says, wrapping his arms around me. I immediately detect whisky.

'I gather you found your way back via the pub you monster?' I laugh.

'Well they said it was going to take them at least an hour to mend the sporran and there was nowhere to go except the pub and the landlord insisted I sample a couple of whiskies,' comes the slightly drawled reply.

'Anyhow, how's the sporran looking?'

'It's come up a treat hen,' he replies, reaching into the bottom of the bag. 'Would you like to stroke it?'

'No I would not. And I was just about to give Angus his injection so stop distracting me.'

'I'm terribly sorry, I'll try to be serious,' Rob replies pulling a straight face which only makes me laugh all the more.

'Oh go away, you're impossible,' I choke.

'Alright. I know when I'm not wanted,' replies my man, swaying off up the stairs.

I go back to the fridge and lift down the small bottle of insulin. Removing the top I push the needle into the liquid and draw up the prescribed dose of four units. The whole routine returns as though it was only yesterday. Holding the syringe up to the light I tap the file to remove any air bubbles and, on making sure there are none left, kneel down beside Angus, gently take hold of the scruff of his neck and carefully insert the needle. It's all over in seconds but the tears are rolling. No, you never get over the loss.

From upstairs I can hear the cabaret continuing. As I glance up the stairs a half-naked husband skips across the landing. As he heads for the bathroom all I can hear is a rather drunken voice singing, 'Donald where's yer troosers?'

MAKE HAY WHILE THE SUN SHINES

'How's about we have a look for a sit in Wales, Chris?' suggests Rob, peering over the top of his glasses from the sofa where he's lying, a copy of a Robert Harris novel in his hands. 'It's ages since we were last there. It would be lovely to go back, maybe somewhere on the Pembrokeshire coast or near the Black Mountains, they're both beautiful parts of the country.'

'I guess it must be at least three years since we did that sit in Brecon,' I reply, thinking back to the last time we'd crossed the English border. 'But you're right, it was beautiful. I'll have a look if you like?'

'It's worth investigating, but just try and find something that doesn't involve sheep this time. A couple of quiet, well-behaved dogs would be fine but I don't want to be playing shepherd again, it was too stressful.'

Our time in Brecon had involved looking after a herd of Welsh sheep and attempting to work with two rather unpleasant sheepdogs. Mother and son did not take kindly to having strangers on their territory and did their best to keep us under their control as much as the sheep. Meg, the mother, spent her time slinking around our ankles watching our every move from her pale, walleyes while her son, Bob, lunged at us threateningly every time we attempted to deal with the sheep. The whole experience had left us exhausted and vowing never to look after livestock again.

I scroll through a number of adverts for sitters but nothing seems to tick the boxes. One in Abergavenny shows a couple of cats sitting on a window-sill next to a wilting, potted geranium and a weed-infested window-box. There are no photos of the house or the interior. I wonder if the owners would consider booking a hotel if there were no images of the building itself or the interior? The blurb says that the cats like to come and go at will, enjoy bringing back presents of half-eaten mice and rabbits and like to sleep on the bed. Yuk!

I swipe down to the next advert which looks much more appealing. Hannah, an elderly lady in her seventies, is searching for someone to look after her rescue dog for ten days. I click on her entry and scroll through the photos. The dog, a collie, intriguingly called Shakya, has a rather unusual but endearing face. He's pure white with a black patch over each eye making him look a bit like a slightly goofy, canine burglar. I've fallen for him already. The photos show a pretty, stone-built, terraced house with roses round the door and a traditional cottage garden full of daisies, fox-gloves and lupins. The interior seems clean and tidy with sequinned wall-hangings of elephants, brightly-coloured throws over the chairs and a line of candles on the bookshelves. I zoom in to examine some of the titles, always a good way of assessing a suitable house-sit. Hannah seems to be into vegan cooking and alternative therapies but also has a few novels by some of my favourite authors.

'What about this Rob? I've found something that I think would suit. Come and look.'

Rob heaves himself up off the sofa and comes to look over my shoulder.

'Oh he's a comical-looking fellow. How old is he?'

'The lady doesn't say, just that he's getting on a bit, but it could be she doesn't know. He's a rescue, so she might not know his exact age. Apparently he's a bit nervous, especially of men.'

'Well, we've managed rescue dogs before, I'm sure we'd cope. It looks a lovely place. I'm happy to give it a go if you'd like to. So where is it?'

'Hay-on-Wye,' I reply, already anticipating the response.

'Oh Chris that's wonderful! Imagine having all those bookshops to browse in. You clever lady. What a brilliant find.'

'Well we haven't got it yet so I'd better get an application in, there's already been a lot of interest. Don't get too excited as we may not get selected.'

It's the following day when I get a message in my mailbox on the website. Hannah seems to have been won over by my application, and, hopefully, by the numerous five star references that we have on our profile. I can't wait to tell Rob when he gets back from doing the shopping. I spend a bit of time investigating what's on in the area in case there's anything happening during our stay and can't believe my eyes when the first website that I visit informs me that it's actually the Hay-on-Wye Literary Festival the very same week. It couldn't get much better.

It's about an hour later that I hear the key in the door and Rob comes staggering in with two heavy carrier bags of shopping. I can hardly contain my excitement.

'I've got some good news for you!' I smile, taking the bags off him and plonking them on the floor.

'You have?'

'We got selected for the sit.'

'Oh that's brilliant. Well done darling.'

'And it gets better,' I smile.

'It does? I can't imagine how.'

'It just so happens to be the Hay Literary Festival at the same time.'

'Oh wow! How absolutely wonderful. Come here and give me a hug. You're a star,' he says, wrapping his arms around me.

'I had no idea, it was just a lucky coincidence but isn't it wonderful?'

'It's better than wonderful, it's bloody marvellous,' he shouts.

'And guess who's appearing?'

'I have no idea, put me out of my misery. I don't think I can cope with any more excitement.'

'Robert Harris!'

'You're joking?' he gasps, unwrapping my arms and looking at me in disbelief.

'No, he's giving a talk about his new book.'

'I think this deserves a celebratory drink my darling wife. I knew I'd got it right when I married you!'

Our journey to Wales is a long one but we arrive, as agreed with Hannah, the day before she's due to leave so that Shakya can get to know us while she's still around and she can show us some of their favourite walks. It's surprisingly warm for May so by the time we pull up outside the house we're both pretty clammy. Our hostess has obviously been keeping an eye out for us as she's already walking down the path to greet us, Shakya barking madly by her side. He's leaping at the gate growling and trying to push his muzzle through the slats.

'Hello!' shouts Hannah, 'don't worry, he's just trying to protect me. He'll be fine. Do come in,' she yells, grabbing Shakya's collar while we sidle past the gate-post. The moment we're in the garden he retreats into the house, eyeing us warily.

'I'm sorry about that,' she says, holding out her hand in greeting. 'It's only because he's nervous. He'll be fine once he's met you. You must be exhausted after your journey, do come in and I'll put the kettle on.'

'Thank you, it has been a long drive. A cuppa would be wonderful,' says Rob.

'I've got peppermint, chamomile or rooibos,' announces Hannah, rooting around in a cupboard and turning round questioningly.

'Er, peppermint please,' replies Rob, looking at me with an alarmed expression.

'Yes, the same for me please, that sounds really refreshing, thank you,' I say, returning Rob's gawky look.

As we sit around the kitchen table attempting to drink our tea I can't help examining Hannah. Her long, grey hair is swept back off her face in a pony-tail that's held in place by a multi-coloured silk scarf. Her flawless skin bares no trace of make-up and she has the sophisticated air of an aristocrat. Her stunning violet-blue eyes are lively and inquisitive, her high cheek-bones giving her face a sculpted look. She's altogether a very handsome woman. I could imagine her being featured in Saga Magazine or modelling for a clothing catalogue as 'the older woman'.

'So where are you heading?' Rob asks. 'Anywhere exciting?'

'Well, I don't know if you'd call it exciting. Not far, only to Pembrokeshire. I'm going on a yoga retreat with some girlfriends. We tend to go every year about this time. Hay is a lovely place most of the year but I hate the crowds during the festival, although it can be fun spotting the celebrities in the bookshops.'

'I expect you've seen many a famous face in the past. The festival's been going ever since I can remember,' I remark.

'Oh yes, 1988 was the first one, although I've only been here since the nineties. I used to offer accommodation back then. I've even had a few authors stay here over the years but that was in the early days when it was much quieter.'

'Oh my!' says Rob, perking up. 'Anyone famous?'

'I suppose that depends on what you mean by famous,' laughs Hannah. 'Margaret Atwood stayed in, let me see, it must have been 95, the year after I came. Then Germaine Greer in 96. You see, we didn't have much in the way of accommodation then and there were only a couple of hotels, so the organisers were keen to find local accommodation. I guess the authors were happy to stay in a cute little cottage.'

'Oh how wonderful! Fancy having such big names staying in your own house. How exciting!' exclaims Rob.

'Anyhow, let me show you your room and maybe you'd like a shower before supper? Then hopefully Shakya will have come out of hiding. Oh, and while I think about it, is there anything you don't eat?'

'I'm afraid I can't manage shellfish,' I reply, and Rob's not keen on aubergine or anchovies but apart from that we're easy.'

'Well I think I said in the details that I'm a vegan so you needn't worry about the shellfish or anchovies. I've got a vegetable curry in the oven if that sounds okay?'

'Mmm, delicious!' replies Rob, much to my surprise. Maybe he's just being polite as he's not very adventurous when it comes to food.

There's a sudden creak as the back door opens and in pads Shakya, his head low, eyes looking forlornly up at us. He stops when he sees Rob and backs off.

'Hello boy. Are you going to come and say hello?' asks Rob, holding out his hand for Shakya to sniff. However, our new furry friend keeps his distance and slides down onto the kitchen floor next to Hannah, head on paws.

'He'll come round eventually, don't worry,' says Hannah. 'He came from a farm up in the hills here. He'd been chained up for months when he was a puppy so he had a really rough start in life. He tends to be wary of men so you might have more success with him initially Christine. Anyhow, why don't you two go and sort yourselves out and I'll see you back down here at, shall we say, seven?'

Our room is a lovely chintzy space with a window overlooking the garden and beyond to the Black Mountains. There's a small vase of fresh flowers on the dressing-table and some fancy toiletries in the bathroom. It's really rather lovely.

'Well this is all very nice darling,' I smile.

'You didn't tell me she was a vegan,' says Rob as we unpack our cases and hang up a few things in the wardrobe. 'Still, she does well on it, she's a good-looking woman for her years.'

'Yes, she is quite stunning. I'm sorry I forgot to tell you about her being a vegan and there's something else I didn't tell you,' I say, plonking myself down on the bed and preparing myself for

Rob's response. 'She doesn't mind us eating vegetarian food but she asked me to agree not to have any meat in the house.'

Rob looks at me askance. 'You did what?'

'Well I knew how keen you were to come to the festival and it was our only option. I'm sure you can cope for a few days darling and we can always have the occasional meal out.'

'No meat? No meat for ten days? You have to be joking Chris. Don't tell me we're going to be living on lentils and tofu or whatever that stuff is. Anyhow, you say she doesn't like meat in the house but what about Shakya? He must eat meat?'

'Er, no actually, he has a vegetarian diet.'

'A vegetarian dog? Oh come off it. You're having me on.'

'Really I'm not, and please keep your voice down,' I say firmly in a loud whisper, 'I don't want Hannah to think we're having an argument.'

'Well I think it's ridiculous,' he whispers back, 'a dog denied its natural diet. And you might deny him his meat but you're not denying me mine!'

It's three days before we manage to make any progress with Shakya but he gradually starts sitting closer to us. Even Rob seems to be winning him over. However, I'm not having much success in winning my man over to the new regime.

'So what delicacy is on the menu this evening may I ask?' a grumpy voice shouts from the sitting-room.

'Za'atar roasted cauliflower, roasted chickpeas and creamy hummus,' I shout back.

'Za'atar? What on earth's za'atar?'

'I haven't a clue but it smells nice.'

'Honestly Chris, this is ridiculous,' he moans, strolling through to the kitchen. 'I mean Hannah wouldn't know if we had the occasional beef-burger or pork chop.'

'No Rob. We signed up to this and we're sticking to it. It would be dishonest to bring meat into the house.'

'I'm sure the occasional sausage would be ok.'

'It would not. A sausage is a sausage.'

'So what's Shakya getting for dinner if he doesn't get a can of proper dog food?'

At the mention of his name Shakya trots into the kitchen and looks up quizzically at Rob.

'According to this,' I say reaching for the bag of kibble, 'quinoa and pumpkin casserole with hemp protein and morenga brown rice, garden veg and herbs. You lucky boy Shakya!' Shakya wags his tail enthusiastically. 'There you are, he's more than happy with his diet.'

'I reckon that's dog abuse old fellow,' say Rob, reaching out and gently stroking the fur on Shakya's neck. 'That owner of yours should be reported. What you need is a huge lump of raw meat and a bone the size of a dinosaur's leg.'

'Well he looks pretty healthy on his diet. He's got a beautiful coat and he's full of energy. Maybe after a few more days you'll be the same,' I laugh. 'So what's on the programme this week, apart from your session with Robert Harris?'

'Not a lot to be honest, most of the sessions were already sold out, but I thought we could have a wander round the bookshops. Anyhow, it looks as though you've got a feast coming up on Friday.'

'Yes, Ruth Hogan, Philip Gwynne-Jones and Rachel Joyce, what a treat! Three of my favourite authors in one day.'

'Well I can take Shakya for a good walk by the river that morning. He really enjoys that walk, especially if I throw stones in the river for him to retrieve. He seems to be coming round gradually and he walked quite well this morning. It's heart-breaking that people could have been so cruel, poor lad. It's hardly surprising he's nervous. Any news from Hannah by the way?'

'No, not a word which I can only assume means she's okay. She's probably totally chilled out saluting the sun on a

Pembrokeshire cliff-top, but I sent her a text and a couple of photos to reassure her that everything's fine.'

The temptation to explore Hay is irresistible so, having walked Shakya, we leave him gnawing on a chew in his basket before wandering up to the town centre. Once a sleepy old market-town on the Welsh border, Hay has evolved over the years into a book-lover's paradise. One by one, old buildings such as the cinema and the fire station have been converted so that there are now over twenty bookshops, many with their own subjects of interest.

'Oh my!' exclaims Rob, looking down the street. 'I don't know where to start. It's a literary heaven!'

'Well that would suit you,' I laugh, pointing across the street to a shop called "Murder and Mayhem." 'There's a poetry bookshop too apparently, you'd enjoy that. Why don't we split up, go for a browse and then meet later for lunch?'

'That's a good idea, then I needn't feel inhibited,' he replies. 'We could meet back here at one o'clock and have a bite at one of the restaurants, there seem to be plenty around.'

'Okay Mr B, see you later. And don't get lost!' I call as he crosses the road and disappears into the bookshop.

It really is a quirky place and I don't think I've ever seen so many books in one spot. It would be easy to spend a whole day in any one of them just browsing and trying to resist the temptation to spend a fortune. We're both trying to be more disciplined about acquiring more books but it rarely works, and I know that I'm the guiltier party. I'm a sucker for classic nineteenth- century novels, especially the old editions, but have to resist the beautiful leather-bound sets that adorn the shelves. The smell in some of the shops is intoxicating, and I can't resist settling down in an armchair with a particularly handsome volume of Wuthering Heights. I'm soon revisiting that dreadful house where the monster, Heathcliff, brutally abuses all who live there, vengeful and unforgiving. How the daughter of a curate managed to create such a harrowing tale is beyond me. I'm out on the moors by Thrushcross Grange, Catherine on her pony, when suddenly someone bumps into the chair where I'm sitting, engrossed in the story, and brings me back to earth. It's only when they apologise that I realise the time. Poor Rob must be wondering where I've got to. I grab my bag and dash down the street to the place where we'd parted and there he is.

'I'm so sorry darling, I got engrossed in a book and totally forgot about the time. Have you been waiting long?' I apologise.

'Only about quarter of an hour, it's alright. I've been having fun people-watching. They're an odd assortment here that's for sure. It seems to be a mix of hippy-types and intellectuals.'

'Well that'll be the local population mixed with the visitors for the festival. Have you spotted anyone famous?'

'No, I can't say I have, but then I wouldn't necessarily recognise many of them. I might know their name or have read their books but I wouldn't know what they looked like. Anyhow, did you have a good time? Find anything interesting?'

'Oh lots, and the most beautiful edition of Wuthering Heights but I was good and resisted. What about you?'

'Ha! Like a mouse in a cheese-shop, but you'll be pleased to hear that I resisted too, apart from one.'

'Oh, so what did you get?'

'Well actually it's for you but you'll have to wait. Let's go and grab some lunch. The eateries all look pretty busy but we could try that place over there,' he says, pointing to a rustic-looking building in one of the side-streets.

We cross the road by the clock-tower and enter the building, what appears to be a converted barn. Strings of hops are draped over the thick, wooden beams and an assortment of old farm implements hangs from the walls. We join the queue at the counter and examine the menu which is written up on chalk-boards on the wall.

'So what do you fancy?' I ask Rob, perusing the choices.

'I'm not really sure. Something with meat, a sausage roll or a pasty perhaps or maybe a steak sandwich or a beef-burger,' he replies.

'Mmmm. Looks as though that might prove difficult,' I reply tentatively. 'I hate to say it darling but I think this might be a vegetarian restaurant.'

'What? You've got to be joking!' replies Rob in horror, his suddenly loud voice attracting the attention of other people in the queue.

'Afraid not. I can't see anything on the menu that has meat. They've got vegetarian sausage-rolls.'

'In which case they're not sausage rolls are they? I don't understand why vegetarians spend all their time eating things that they then pretend are something else. Oh alright, I guess I'll just have a piece of quiche and some salad,' he replies sulkily. 'It's too late to go somewhere else at this hour. I'll go and find a table. Oh, and I'll have a glass of red wine please,' and with that Rob makes his way through the crowded tables to a bench against the back wall.

I join him at the table with our order precariously balanced on a tray, already anticipating the reaction.

'I'm sorry sweetheart but it's a cup of tea, they don't sell wine,' I announce hesitantly as I squeeze onto the bench beside him.

'What? For goodness sake what's wrong with the place? No meat, no wine? I hope it isn't something disgusting like chamomile tea?'

'Just think yourself lucky I didn't order you an avocado and spinach smoothie Mr Moanalot!' I laugh.

Just as we're about to tuck into our lunch a rather distinguished gentleman, probably in his sixties, weaves his way through the tables and, having surveyed the chaos, makes his way over to our table.

'I'm so sorry to intrude, but would you mind terribly if I sit at your table? There don't seem to be any other spaces.'

'No, of course not,' replies Rob. 'Please, let me give you some more space,' he says, moving his plate further along the table. 'It is rather busy isn't it? I suppose it's all the visitors.'

'Yes, it seems like a good turn-out,' replies our fellow-diner. 'So are you two locals or are you here for the festival?'

'Here for the festival, but doing a bit of dog-sitting at the same time,' replies Rob between mouthfuls.

'Oh that's nice, what sort of dog is it?' asks the man.

'He's a collie and he's gorgeous,' I reply. 'He's white with two black eyes and looks like a burglar, but he's so bright. We've really fallen for him.'

'Yes, they're clever dogs aren't they? I used to have a border collie called Rosie. Don't think I'll ever get over losing her,' he says sadly.

'No, it's tough. After all they're family aren't they?' I reply.

We munch our way through our lunch making polite conversation with our guest and, having drunk our tea, get ready to make a move.

'Do excuse us but we'd better get back to our charge, he's probably got his legs crossed by now,' laughs Rob. 'It's been nice meeting you,' he says and reaches out to shake the man's hand.

'And you too,' he replies, rising from his seat politely. 'Enjoy the festival!'

'Thank you,' we reply in unison.

Once outside I'm bursting to speak to Rob.

'Do you know who I think that was?'

'Who are you talking about?'

'The man that we've just had lunch with.'

'No, who?'

'Robert Harris!'

'What? Are you sure?' asks Rob, now rooted to the spot with a bewildered look on his face. 'You mean, I've just had lunch with Robert Harris?'

'I think so. I'm not a hundred percent sure, but it would seem quite possible with him being on the programme for the festival wouldn't it?'

'But why didn't you say before?'

'Well I could hardly say, "Excuse me but are you by any chance Robert Harris?" now could I?'

'Why ever not?'

'Well I'd have felt a bit stupid, especially if it wasn't him.'

'And I shook hands with him!'

'Well if it really was him, then yes.'

'I'm not going to wash until we find out for sure.'

'Noodle!' I laugh. 'Let's get back and rescue poor Shakya before he has an accident.'

Arriving back at the house Shakya is beside himself at our return. He dives around, tail wagging frantically and wants to wrap his paws round my neck. He's clearly settled with us after the somewhat shaky start.

'Oh he's so adorable Rob. Can we smuggle him home?' I ask, opening the back door to let him into the garden.

'I don't think Hannah would be too pleased. Anyhow, let's do a bit of Googling,' he says, reaching for the iPad and passing it over to me. I type in Robert Harris and yes, there he is. Our man.

'It was him!' I reply triumphantly.

'Oh that's brilliant Chris, but what a missed opportunity.'

'But it must be quite a relief for him not to be recognised and quizzed about his books, you know, just to be normal occasionally.'

'I suppose so, but what about the dog he mentioned, Rosie wasn't it?'

'Let me have a look. Yes, here we are. Aw, he posted her death on Twitter in 2018 and there's her photo too.'

'Let me see. Oh, what a sweet face bless her. It must have hit him hard. He was a nice man wasn't he? Oh, and by the way, before I forget, here's the little something that I got for you,' he says, handing me a carrier-bag.

'Oh, I'd totally forgotten,' I reply, wondering what treat there is in store. I reach into the bag and pull out a large book. On turning it over I have to suppress a smile when I see the title: "Let's Eat Meat by Tom Parker-Bowles." 'Oh Rob, you don't give up do you?' I laugh.

'No, I just thought you might be tempted by some of the recipes,' he replies looking coyly at me.

'Anyhow, recipes aside, I think we might need to get a certain someone out for a W-A-L-K!'

The week scuds by but Friday can't come soon enough. The chance of seeing not one, but three, of my favourite authors in one session is something I would never have dreamed possible. I get my books together in the hope of getting them signed and, as the show-ground is a bit of a hike, decide to set off in good time in the hope of spotting some of the many celebrities who are in town.

'Don't forget your books,' Rob reminds me when he sees me getting my things together. 'Or your hat, it's going to be a warm one and you have to look the literary type,' he laughs handing me my straw hat.

'I've got the books in my bag already. I'd hardly miss an opportunity like this would I? And do I assume that you two are going down to the river?'

'Yes, we like the river don't we boy?' says Rob as Shakya pads into the kitchen panting. 'It's surprisingly warm for May and it helps to cool him down. He loves retrieving stones from the water don't you boy? So we'll see you later. Enjoy your session darling.'

It is warm and after about only half a mile I'm beginning to wish that I'd worn something cooler. We usually travel light, even when we have the car, but my wardrobe is proving rather inappropriate for such a warm day. As I stroll along the route to the festival the numbers are starting to build up, and there's a really lively atmosphere with excited voices. It's a mixed crowd and it's fun just listening in to the conversations going on around me. It's only when I step away from a group of rather excited festival-goers that I realise that my phone is ringing. The ring-tone tells me it's Rob. No doubt he's locked himself out or got lost. I rummage in my bag, step aside from the crowd, and answer it.

'Hello darling, what can I do for you?'

'Chris, I need you here immediately. I'm down by the bridge. I think I've killed Shakya!'

'I'm on my way!' I reply, thrusting the phone back in my bag.

My instinct isn't to ask questions but to turn and run, retracing my route back to the cottage and the pull-in where we've parked the car. Needless to say I'm running against the flow of the crowd so it slows my progress, I keep bumping into people who are understandably annoyed by what appears to be my carelessness. I brush against someone's shoulder and my hat gets knocked to the ground but I rush on without retrieving it, my heart pounding. I can't begin to imagine what's happened. Killed Shakya, how? I can only imagine he's drowned, what else could possibly have happened? But how? Maybe he went in too deep and got carried down the river? Rob wouldn't have been able to go after him as he's not a strong swimmer. I search in my bag for the car keys while I'm running, my mind racing, and by the time I reach the car my palms are sweating. I leap in, start the engine, my hands trembling, and within minutes I'm by the bridge. I manage to pull the car off the road, abandoning it at the road-side. I can see Rob below on the shingle bank with Shakya lying at his feet, a couple of men standing over him. I slither down the bank to his side, unable to hold back the tears.

'Oh my God, what's happened?' I cry as I look down at the sodden, limp body.

'I was throwing stones for him to fetch out of the river. One went up in the air but he was just standing there waiting for it to land and couldn't see that it was above him. It landed on his head and he went under the water. I thought I'd killed him Chris, but he's still alive. I think he's just badly concussed but we need to get him to a vet quickly.'

'I can show you the way,' interrupts one of the men. 'Let's get him in your car and then just follow me. Mine's the white pick-up truck just in front of yours.'

Lifting a wet, limp dog is no easy feat, but between the three of us we manage to carry Shakya up the bank and get him into the back of the car. A small crowd has gathered on the bridge and is watching our every move. I manage to turn the car round and immediately tag on behind the white pick-up. We follow him onto an industrial estate where the vet's surgery is and, between us, manage to unload a very groggy dog. Having delivered us safely our helper drives off with a friendly wave but with a concerned look on his face.

Rob's visibly shaken. 'I think he's coming round Chris, he's just opened his eyes. Oh thank God. Pray that he's going to be okay.'

I squeeze Rob's shoulder, realising just how traumatic the whole thing has been and push open the door into the surgery. A veterinary nurse has already picked up on us and realised that we're an emergency case. I explain what's happened and she quickly ushers us into a consulting room. Poor Shakya is clearly recovering but waking up in such strange surroundings isn't helping him. His whole body starts to tremble and he starts to whimper, thrusting his nose into Rob's hand. Rob strokes his head, trying to calm him.

'You're alright boy, everything's going to be fine.'

At that moment an elderly man with thinning ginger hair, ruddy cheeks and very few teeth, shuffles into the consulting room. We assume that he is, in fact, the vet due to his attire. He's wearing a long, blue apron and a pair of large rubber gloves and looks as though he's just returned from having his hand stuck up a cow's backside.

'So what's been going on yur then?' he asks, raising his eyebrows and looking down at the shivering Shakya. 'Bit of a bang on the head is it?'

Rob explains the drama while the vet lifts Shakya's head gently and shines a light in his eyes. He removes his gloves and runs his hands slowly down Shakya's body exploring his ribs before listening to his heart. Rob looks across the table at me, his eyes welling up.

'Well, I think he's got off lightly, lucky boy,' announces the vet. 'Could have been nasty. He's concussed but there's no damage that I can see. I suggest you keep him nice and quiet for the rest of the day. Any problems, vomiting or seeming confused, and you bring him straight back yur, but I reckon he's going to be okay.'

I can see the relief on Rob's face. He's so thankful I'm half expecting him to give the vet a hug. Shakya manages to heave himself onto his front legs but hangs his head and, with sad eyes, looks imploringly at Rob. Between us we manage to lift him down from the metal table and, after walking him gently round the waiting-room a few times to make sure he's steady, we're able to leave. Poor Shakya can't get out fast enough, despite his recent brush with death. We lift him up gently into the back of the car where he immediately snuggles into our picnic-rug with a deep sigh, his head on his paws.

Rob remains pretty quiet for the rest of the day, Shakya by his side. He's clearly been seriously unnerved by the experience.

'You okay sweetheart?' I ask, handing him a mug of tea.

'Yes, I am now, but that was the most awful experience Chris. It's bad enough when something like that happens to your own dog, but when it's someone else's pet in your care it's even worse. And you missed your event at the festival, I'm so sorry.'

'It isn't the end of the world, and at least there was a happy ending. Anyhow, I'd better get on with dinner or it'll be bedtime before we eat.'

'What are we having?'

'Sausages.'

'Rob almost leaps out of his chair. Sausages? Oh Chris, that's exactly what I need after today. Thank you so much darling. My body's crying out for some meat. Will it take long?'

'Half an hour max if you can wait that long,' I call back from the kitchen, unwrapping the Linda McCartney vegetarian sausages from their wrapper, and carefully burying the packaging in the bin. I can't wait to see if the rehydrated, textured, soya protein passes the test.

THERE'S NO PLACE LIKE ROME

'Well this doesn't bode well Chris,' announces Rob, running his hands through his hair and looking exasperated.

'What doesn't?'

'There's been an earthquake in Italy, and an air traffic control strike by the French.'

'Oh no! So where exactly is the earthquake?'

'Close to Rome. According to this article it hit 4.5 on the Richter scale and made areas of the inner city shake, including some of the historic monuments. '

'Crikey, that does sound serious! But mind you, earthquakes are pretty common in Italy and as for the French, they're always going on strike, especially at times when they can cause the most disruption. Anyhow, we can hardly cancel the sit at this late stage. I'm sure it'll all be fine, and there's no way we're not going after all the work I've had to put in to organising everything, and, besides, I've been really looking forward to it. Christmas in Rome and New Year in Venice, what more could you want?'

Our new home was to be an apartment in the Trastevere area of Rome, a city we'd never had the chance to visit. According to the travel guides the area was considered to be the Bohemian district, attracting artists and writers with its café culture and artisan shops. Situated on the third floor with views down to the river Tiber, the apartment was described as luxurious and given a five-star rating by a previous sitter who reported that it was 'amazing'. The owners, an Italian interior designer and an American creative analyst, (whatever one of those is), left us feeling pretty confident that this was going to be an incredible opportunity to explore one of Italy's most beautiful cities.

In spite of earthquakes and Frenchmen on strike, we arrive in the capital on Friday 13th December, eager to explore, for us, a yet undiscovered part of Italy. After a long and tiring journey from the airport by bus and then taxi, we drop our cases at our hotel and head off to find our new home and meet the owners. The narrow back streets are confusing but after wandering around the area for some time, searching for the right address, we eventually find the street and our apartment block or 'palazzo' as the Italians call them. On ringing the doorbell we narrowly miss being run over while waiting on the doorstep for the door to be opened remotely. The pavement is incredibly narrow and the traffic fast and furious. As we hear a voice over the tannoy the lock opens and we enter a rather dingy, communal hallway, the individual letterboxes for the various apartments overflowing with junk mail, much of which has migrated to the floor. On finding the lift we press the button to ascend and wait. The lift eventually arrives, and, as the door opens, a very large man in a Lazio football shirt squeezes out, scowls at us, and heads for the front door, leaving behind him a strong smell of sweat and garlic. We step inside and press the button for the the third floor. We're carried slowly and jerkily upwards, and as the lift doors clank open, we wander along a stone-flagged corridor searching for number 47. After fighting our way past a somewhat over-enthusiastic display of artificial plants outside a neighbouring door, we ring the bell.

Our arrival is met by a deep, throaty bark, as our new charge comes to investigate. The heavy, wooden door rattles as a man's voice from within shouts something that we're unable to hear because of the noise, as he grapples with the security lock. After much clunking the door opens and we're greeted by a chunky, young man with floppy, dark hair and a warm smile.

'Hi you guys, come in!' he says, quickly grabbing our new charge by the collar. 'Let me close the door before this beast of mine tries to escape.'

The 'beast', a somewhat overweight, chocolate Labrador with a decidedly downcast expression, immediately starts to bark the place down. Our host invites us to take a seat in one of the orange bucket-chairs by the window then disappears into another room. He returns with a chew which is grabbed by the dog who then trots off down the passageway.

'That was Gianna as you've probably guessed, and I'm Gus. Welcome to Rome! I hope you've had a good journey,' he says, wiping his hands on his trousers.

'Long and tiring, but we made it,' replies Rob.

'So is this your first time in Rome?' he asks, settling down on the bright purple settee.

'Yes,' I reply, 'we're really looking forward to exploring. There's so much to see.'

I glance quickly round the room, taking in our new surroundings. Two lime green, plastic arm chairs, a glass coffee table and a few bookshelves filled mainly with untidy piles of paper and magazines. It's a bit spartan and utilitarian for an interior designer, but maybe it's supposed to be minimalist. Who knows?

'I'm sorry we couldn't offer you a bed for the night, but as I said in my email, I'm afraid we've only got the one room,' apologises Gus.

'No worries,' I reply. 'It's a treat for us to have the luxury of a night in a hotel before we move in. When are you off?'

'Unfortunately really early. We have to fly to Amsterdam to catch a connecting flight so we'll be leaving about four in the morning. I'm sorry Rosa couldn't be here to meet you but she's having to work late to tie up a few things before we go.'

'And you're going back to the US I gather?' queries Rob.

'Yes, back home to New York to see my folks. We haven't seen them for a couple of years and they aren't getting any younger. Anyhow, I think we're more or less ready. My wife seems to think it necessary to take half her wardrobe on a trip whereas I can manage with an overnight bag!'

I can't help but think that it's the other way round in our house, but decide to keep quiet about the size of Rob's suitcase.

At this point Gianna comes ambling back into the room, thankfully calmer, and inspects us both before scrambling up onto the sofa where she flops down taking up most of the space, her head on Gus's knee. However, she keeps her eyes open and watches our every move.

'She's a lovely girl,' says Gus, fondling her head, 'but like all Labs she's greedy, so what ever you do don't leave any food within reach or she'll snaffle it. I'm afraid walking her round here is a pain because there's so much junk thrown down on the sidewalk. Oh and she pulls.'

My mind is cast back to our very first house-sit with our furry friend Eddie the Beagle. He was a canine hoover too. This is going to be fun.

'Just a couple of things Gus. Where's the nearest supermarket? We're going to need a few things tomorrow to set us up for the week,' asks Rob.

'Oh no problem, there's one at the end of the road and I'm sure Rosa'll be leaving a few bits for you in the fridge.'

'And what about the rubbish? Where does that go?'

'I'm afraid you have to take it to the big bins down on the main road. We don't have a collection as there are huge skips there for the trash, but I'm afraid the refuse collectors are on strike, so the streets are pretty disgusting at the moment. They haven't collected anything for five weeks now. Crikey I'm not really selling this to you am I?' he laughs.

'No worries,' replies Rob. 'And the keys?'

'Gee, I'm glad you reminded me. There's a set here for you,' he says, reaching over to the table and handing Rob a small, leather wallet. 'But I'm warning you, this door can be a bit temperamental. We all have these heavy-duty security locks so please make sure you lock up before you go out and close the outer door downstairs in the lobby. You can't be too careful round here.'

'Well, I think you gave us all the other information we need by email, including Gianna's routine, so we'll get out of your way,' I say, getting up from my seat. 'I'm sure you've got a lot to do before you leave. We'll be here first thing in the morning to get her out and I'll send you a text to let you know we've arrived.'

'Oh that would be great. Rosa's a worrier so the occasional photo of Gianna would be welcome, just to reassure her that it's all going well,' replies Gus, extracting himself from the settee where Gianna turns on her side with a loud sigh and stretches out her legs.

'Of course, that's no problem,' replies Rob, leaning over to stroke Gianna before heading for the door. 'We'll see you tomorrow lovely lady and safe journey Gus, enjoy your trip!'

We return to the palazzo the following morning just before eight o'clock, keen to get Gianna out for a quick walk round the block. We realise that dogs are pretty quick at picking up on what's going on when suitcases are involved and want to get back to the apartment in case she's fretting. It proves quite a challenge to fit both us and our suitcases into the lift, especially as Rob has insisted on bringing the biggest suitcase that we possess.

'Why on earth you had to bring that hulking great thing I do not know Rob. You'd think we were going to be away for months,' I grumble as the lift lurches its way up to the third floor.

'Well it is winter, and winter clothes are thick and bulky, and we are here for three weeks. Just because you travel light it doesn't mean to say that I have to.'

'And quite why you need to wear your Borsalino I don't know. Couldn't you have managed with a woolly hat like most people?'

'Darling, this is the capital of fashion. I intend to look stylish even if you don't.'

'I hate to argue with you Mr Baird, but I think you'll find that's Milan?' I smirk.

Our discussion ends abruptly as the lift shudders to a halt at the third floor. Dragging our cases behind us, we make our way along the corridor, past the potted plants, to our door where Rob fumbles in his coat pocket for the keys.

'Right! Well here we are,' he says placing the key in the lock. His voice immediately alerts Gianna who has come to the other side of the door and is greeting us with her best throaty bark.

'It's alright Gianna, it's only us,' he calls, attempting to turn the key in the lock. He removes it, examines it and tries again. 'It doesn't seem to want to turn Chris,' he says, screwing his face up as he has another go. 'Maybe I've tried to put it in the wrong way,' he says fumbling with the key and trying again. 'Nope, it doesn't want to turn.'

The barking is becoming more frantic and I can't imagine we're going to be too popular with the other residents in the block.

'Here, let me have a go,' I say taking the keys. 'Gus did warn us that it could be tricky. There must be a knack to it.' But, however hard I try, I can't get the key to turn either.

'Let me have another shot at it,' says Rob, inserting the key in the lock and pushing forcefully against the heavy door with his shoulder. 'Maybe the door doesn't sit properly in the frame and you have to help it a bit?'

Twenty minutes later we're still struggling to open the door and poor Gianna's barking has reached a crescendo. A neighbour, presumably leaving the building for work, gives us an irritated scowl as she squeezes past us and mutters something under her breath.

'Can't you contact Gus and ask him what the mode of attack is?' asks Rob, his face now flushed from his efforts. 'There's clearly some technique that I'm just not mastering.'

'I could try, but my guess is that they're probably in the air by now, and there doesn't seem much point in worrying them the minute we get here.'

'Well I reckon you'll need to call a lock-smith Chris. It seems the only answer.'

'I notice it's me as usual,' I shout, trying to make my voice heard over the incessant barking. 'And how the heck am I supposed to know the Italian for lock-smith in order to search for a number?'

'Well what's the Italian for key?'

'*Il chiave*, why?'

'Because if you …'

We're suddenly interrupted as the door directly opposite ours opens and a rather frail, elderly gentleman peers out at us looking somewhat exasperated. I smile apologetically and try to explain our situation in my best Italian.

'*Mi dispiace Signor, ma non possiamo aprire la porta.*'

He shuffles carefully down three steps into the corridor and gestures for the keys which Rob duly hands over. Bending over and placing the key in the lock he turns it gently, places his hand on the door-knob and in one easy action, opens the door. We thank him profusely and, without saying a word, he turns round, carefully climbs the three steps to his apartment and shuts the door behind him. Gianna is already out on the landing, tail wagging furiously and whining with pleasure. She's clearly been as traumatised as we have.

'Oh my goodness, what a way to start!' exclaims Rob, dragging his suitcase into the sitting-room. 'We're going to have to master that before we go out again or we won't be able to risk leaving this one behind,' he says, flopping down onto the sofa where he's quickly joined by Gianna who immediately rolls over inviting him to tickle her tummy. 'Well Gianna,' he says rubbing the proffered chest, 'we made it and we're going to be good friends aren't we girl?'

Gianna responds by clawing at Rob's arm with one of her paws insisting on more tummy tickles.

'Well I suggest we take our stuff into the bedroom and then we'd better get this lady out,' I say, heading along the corridor.

Not having seen any further than the sitting-room on our first visit, we're somewhat surprised to find that the bedroom is incredibly cramped. There's only just enough space to get round the bed, and there's not even an inch of room in the one small cupboard in which to hang our clothes.

'Maybe there's hanging space in the room next door?' I suggest. But no, the room next door is so full of junk that there's no room for any of our stuff. 'You'll just have to drape your things over the end of the bed or maybe over a chair in the sitting-room darling,' I suggest, already anticipating the response.

'But what about my cords and my Armani jacket Chris? They're going to get ruined. I can't leave them next door or they'll be covered in dog-hair.'

'Well maybe we can buy a few coat-hangers while we're out and then you can hang them from the curtain rail.'

'That would be helpful if there was a curtain rail,' replies Rob, hands on hips. 'Anyhow, I'm dying for a wee. Excuse me while I pop to the bathroom.' Within seconds he's back by my side. 'There is absolutely no way that I am using that loo Chris. It's disgusting.'

'In what way disgusting?' I ask, but on entering the bathroom have to agree that it really is foul. 'I agree, that is gross! I wonder if there's any bleach in the kitchen? Hang on and I'll go and see.'

'I'm not staying in here a minute longer than I have to, thank you very much,' replies Rob following me into the kitchen.

The doors to the cupboard under the sink are actually hanging on a length of brown parcel tape and, on opening them, I quickly establish that there is neither bleach nor any cleaning materials.

'Oh this is dire Rob. We're going to have to clean this place before we can eat anything. We'd better add a few cleaning materials to the shopping-list. How about we just dump our stuff and go and get some basic supplies down the road?'

'That's a good idea but what about the door? Gianna needs to go out for a walk, she's been stuck in here and distressed and she's probably bursting for a wee like me so we can hardly leave her behind.'

'Okay. The plan is that we have a go at the door to make sure we can get back in, then we both go to the supermarket and take Gianna with us. You can hang about outside while I do the shopping. How's that?'

'Excellent. I'll have another go at the door now.'

But try as we may we're unable to fathom out how to lock the door securely on the barrel lock. It looks like five solid brass cylinders that slide across and render the door impregnable.

'It's no use Chris. We're just going to have to risk locking it on the single lock or chances are we'll be stuck outside on the landing again.'

'Okay, well let's leave it like that and we'll see if we can work it out when we get back.'

And so, with an eager Gianna attached to her lead, we squeeze into the lift and head down to the ground floor. Fortunately for Rob our door is directly opposite a public loo so he calls in to relieve himself. We set off for the supermarket, Gianna pulling Rob impatiently along the pavement alongside the busy traffic, nose to the ground and lurching at discarded food on the pavement. She's a strong dog and I can see that walking her is going to be a challenge.

Leaving Rob outside with Gianna sniffing all along the shop front, I grab a basket and head for the deli counter. Having over-indulged in salami, prosciutto, fresh pasta and a couple of local cheeses I head for the bread counter only to collide with a trolley in which is seated an adorable golden-haired labradoodle. I'm somewhat confused. A dog in a trolley? The Brits would go mad and rant about hygiene. I'm enthralled. The lady pushing the trolley has obviously picked up on my surprise and smiles warmly at me. It's then that I see a picture of a dog attached to the trolley and the words, '*Per trasportami utilizza questo carrello*'. So you can actually put your dog in the trolley while you shop. What a brilliant idea!

With two large bags loaded with enough food to feed an army, a battery of cleaning materials, a couple of bottles of wine, a large bottle of water, a bottle of bleach and some rubber gloves, I head for the exit only to find Rob looking exhausted with Gianna straining on the lead and getting in everybody's way.

'Thank goodness you're back. She's been horrendous. She's been dragging me all over the place Chris. She's already eaten half a pizza that someone dropped. Let's get her home before my arm gets pulled out of its socket.'

'Well if you can manage one of these bags I'll take her for a while if you want.'

'I think it's probably better that I keep her love, she really is strong, she'll have you off your feet. Can you manage those bags?'

'I think so, I'll shout if I need to stop.'

The walk back is exhausting, not just because of the weight of the bags but because the place is so crowded. I'm constantly pushed and jostled and have to keep stepping off the pavement to avoid injury which results in angry drivers leaning on their horns. By the time we get back to the apartment we're both shattered. It's a relief to get into the lobby and close the outer door behind us.

'Thank goodness for that. I've got arms like an orangutan after that walk,' I pant, putting the bags down by the lift door. I press the button but, after what seems like an age, there is no sign of the lift. 'It's taking forever,' I sigh, 'and all I want to do is collapse and have a nice cup of coffee.' It's then that I notice the sign on the door that reads, "*Fuori servizio*". 'Oh no! I don't believe it,' I wail.

'Why, what is it?'

'The sign on the door. It means out of order.'

'You're joking?'

'I wish I was but I'm afraid I'm not.'

'Oh God, we're going to have to climb all those stairs Chris.'

'I know, but there's nothing else for it, come on.' And so we begin the ascent, Gianna pulling Rob up the stairs faster than he can manage, her under-carriage dragging over the steps and me lugging two heavy carrier bags full of shopping. We manage two flights before having to stop for a breather.

'Crikey,' pants Rob. 'I'm absolutely cream-crackered.'

'You are? Well at least you're getting pulled upstairs. Let's swap. I'll take her for a while and you carry this lot.' And so we change places and start the next flight of stone stairs.

'Twenty-four, twenty-five, twenty-six,' comes the breathless voice behind me while I try to slow Gianna down by hanging onto the metal handrail. 'Twenty-seven, twenty-eight, twenty-nine ... I'm going to have to stop Chris.'

I'm only too relieved to pause myself. This is proving a challenge we could both do without. 'Surely we must be nearly there? I'm trying to work out how many flights there are.'

'Well we live on the third floor and we're number 47. That's all I know.'

'But these doors are still in the twenties,' I pant, pulling furiously on Gianna's lead. And it's then that the penny drops. 'I hate to say it Rob but Italian floors are numbered differently to British ones, so our third floor is actually the fourth floor.'

'Good grief. You mean we've got more stairs to climb?'

'Lots more I'm afraid. Come on, let's go. We can do this,' I pant, not actually believing anything of what I'm saying. And so we take a deep breath and start to climb the next flight of steps, every one a challenge. Seventy-one, seventy-two, seventy-three and at last we arrive on our landing. Seventy-three cruel, unforgiving, stone steps. I can feel my heart banging away and am convinced that my blood-pressure has gone up a few points.

'Oh my God, I think I'm going to collapse Chris,' pants Rob, sitting down on the top step while Gianna comes to lick the sweat off his face. 'I hope to goodness they get that lift fixed sharpish. I don't think I could manage that too often. Anyhow, let's get this door open and get the food in the fridge,' he gasps, heaving himself up off the step.

Fortunately the key turns in the lock first time so we head for the kitchen and dump the bags on the table out of Gianna's reach. Knowing that there's food in there she begins her barking repertoire and stands, paws up on the table, nosing at the bags. Too exhausted to be upset by the noise I open the fridge door only to be met by a disgusting smell. It's empty apart from a mouldy cauliflower and, in one of the plastic drawers, a polythene bag full of green slime that might once have been salad.

'Oh this is the pits Rob. Fancy leaving it in this state when you've got people staying in your house. It's disgusting. I'm going to have to clean the whole thing before we can put anything in there.'

So while I set too to wash down the interior, Rob goes to collapse on the settee. Gianna, who has given up barking as she wasn't getting any attention, scrambles up beside him and very soon they're both fast asleep and snoring in harmony.

It's a good hour later when I finally finish disinfecting the bathroom, cleaning the fridge, scrubbing the sink and worktops and sterilising two of everything so that we can eat. Too exhausted to be creative I decide just to cook some pasta for lunch so search the cupboards for a large saucepan. Finding one buried under other kitchen implements I recoil as, on removing the lid, I find it encrusted with something green and hard that I assume must be baked-on spinach. And so it's back on with the rubber gloves and another assault with hot, soapy water. This is not going well.

'Maybe we should just try and find alternative accommodation?' suggests Rob over lunch. 'I mean it is pretty awful here and there's no way we can tackle those stairs a couple of times a day in the hope that they get the lift working again.'

'The problem with that is that it has to be dog-friendly self-catering and it's Christmas.'

'I know but it's got to be worth a try. Most hotels in Italy accept dogs. Why don't we have a look online and see if we can find something?'

I'm impressed by the use of the word 'we' as Rob is a master at delegating and getting me to organise everything. He must be fed up. However, an hour later and we've given up the idea. Although there are rooms available the prices are sky-high because it's Christmas and are way out of our budget.

'I guess we're stuck here for the duration then,' sighs Rob finishing his espresso. 'We're just going to have to make the most of it. How about we go and explore? It might lift our spirits and Gianna's going to need a good walk. We could go down to the Trastavere and maybe even have an early dinner there to save cooking?'

'Sounds good to me. A cosy little trattoria would suit me fine. I'll go and get my coat.'

The notes that Gus and Rosa have left for us suggest that it's an easy walk down to the Trastevere. It's the word 'down' that troubles me because obviously 'down' implies that there must also be an 'up'.

'I suppose we could always get a bus back up,' suggests Rob.

'But where from and where to? We don't know the area at all yet darling. We wouldn't have a clue where we were and I don't know if we can take a dog on the bus.'

'I'd be surprised if you couldn't with it being such a dog-friendly country.'

'Oh crikey! That's a point! I've just realised that we're supposed to be carrying a muzzle for her. Don't you remember when we did that sit in Tuscany we found it was the law?'

'Yes but nobody paid any notice to it. Laws are only made to be broken in this country. You should know that by now.'

'But we were in the back of beyond then, not in the capital city. I'd better see if I can find one.' After much ferreting around in drawers and cupboards I return with a grubby-looking plastic muzzle. 'I guess this is it. I'll stuff it in my bag just in case.'

And so we set off to explore, Gianna pulling us eagerly, and frighteningly quickly, down the seventy-three steps. Narrowly avoiding being run over we cross the road and make our way through the residential area. It isn't a particularly attractive area but after a couple of streets we eventually find a long flight of stairs leading down to the lower level.

'Good grief, is anything here on the flat?' calls Rob as Gianna sets off bouncing down the steps dragging him behind her.

'Well, if you remember your ancient history, Rome was built on seven hills and I guess this is one of them,' I call back, moving to one side to allow a jogger to get past.

The Trastevere proves to be an interesting area with a vibrant café culture and interesting shops but after a couple of hours we're both tired and decide to brave the walk home rather than eat out. Gianna is proving a handful as she walks nose to the ground and refuses to budge if she finds anything interesting. Rob is clearly becoming fed up with being dragged everywhere and his hands and shoulders are suffering as a result of the constant pulling.

'I wish you'd let me take her for a while, she's going to do you a damage.'

'I think she already has to be honest, my shoulder's aching

like mad and I think I've pulled a chest muscle.'

'Well here, let me have her,' I say, taking the lead off him. Gianna immediately disappears around the back of a tree and I end up hugging it as I try to pass the lead from one hand to another. The way home is along an extremely busy road so I have to keep her on a short lead to avoid her bolting into the traffic but the pavement is blocked at regular intervals because of the mountains of rubbish that are building up at the communal bins.

'This is no fun,' I shout to Rob above the noise of the traffic. 'Why don't we cross the road here and then we can walk through that park over there?'

'Alright, good idea,' he shouts back, 'but let me take her again while we cross the road.'

I hand the lead back to Rob as we wait at the appointed crossing for the green man to appear. As the lights change we set off hurriedly across the road but, to our horror, halfway across Gianna decides that she doesn't want to walk any further and flops down on the crossing with all four legs splayed out on the tarmac. Rob immediately tries to heave her up off the road by pulling on the lead but she isn't having any of it and refuses to budge.

'Gianna, come on!' he shouts frantically bending down and trying to lift her by the collar. 'Well don't just stand there for God's sake Chris, come and help me!'

Partly in shock I rush to his side and between us we attempt to scoop 25 kilos of Labrador up off the road. Although the spectacle is causing much amusement to some of the drivers, those who can't see what's going on have already lost patience and, as the lights have now changed to green, are leaning on their horns Italian style. But Gianna is adamant she's not going anywhere.

'Give her a treat!' shouts Rob. I reach into my pocket and, now shaking as a result of the drama, proffer a treat and wave it in front of her nose. After a nano-second of contemplation our beast is on all four paws and following me at a trot as I tempt her across the road to the comparative safety of the pavement.

'Oh my God that was so humiliating Chris. What on earth was that about for goodness sake?'

'I guess she'd just had enough, but what a place to collapse! It couldn't have been worse. Let's head for home. I don't know about you but I'm exhausted after that exhibition.'

Realising that we're going to have to cross the road again further along, we prepare ourselves for a repeat performance but have the treats at hand to keep her moving. Fortunately our plan works and she trots across following my hand and is duly rewarded on the other side.

I'd already worked out the route home before leaving the apartment and know that there's a long and winding route that will take us gradually back up the hill but I'd also spotted a short-cut on the map.

'We're looking for the viale Glorioso,' I call to Rob who is being pulled into the dirty doorway of a shop.

'There it is!' he shouts, pointing ahead to a sign on the side of a tall apartment block. However, our excitement is short-lived when, on reaching the corner, we discover that the viale Glorioso consists of what appears to be an endless flight of steps some twenty metres wide. 'Oh no! I don't believe it Chris. Do you mean we have to climb that lot?'

'I'm afraid it looks like it darling. I'm so sorry, the steps didn't show up on the map, it just looked like any other street.'

'Well I don't suppose we have much choice do we?'

'Not really, I wouldn't have a clue which bus to catch. It's either this or we follow this road all the way round but the steps'll take at least a mile off the walk, what's more it's going to be dark soon. Come on, we can do it,' I say, trying my best to sound encouraging. And so we begin the climb.

A hundred and twenty-six steps later we arrive at the top

end of the via Dandolo, sweating under our winter clothing.

'I don't think I can walk any further Chris,' wails Rob, removing his scarf. 'I'm absolutely worn out and if our lift still isn't working I shall simply sit down and cry.'

'Come on sweetheart, we're nearly there. Let's just pray that it's been fixed.'

Much to our relief on returning to our palazzo there is no sign on the lift door and it's only a matter of minutes before we're on our landing and turning the key in the door. We both head for the settee and collapse in a heap. Gianna deciding to haul herself up and squeeze in between us, pushing me aside with her back legs. With a loud sigh she falls asleep.

It must be a couple of hours later that I wake up, the room in darkness, to find Rob and Gianna still soundo. I wander over to the window and look down into the street below. The attendant at the public loo opposite is standing outside, propped up against the wall, smoking a cigarette. He must sense that he's being watched as he glances up and scowls. I move away and put the light on at which point Rob, still dressed in his coat, wakes up and yawns loudly.

'*Buona sera bello*,' I smile. 'I guess we needed that!'

'Well it has been a bit of an exhausting day and my body aches from head to foot. I reckon we might need an early night.'

'Not before we've taken Gianna round the block before bed.'

'Oh no! I'd forgotten about that.'

'Don't worry, I'll take her, I don't mind.'

'If you think I'm going to let my wife out on the streets of Rome on her own, especially in the dark, then you are very much mistaken Mrs Baird. You might get whisked off by an Italian gigolo or get your bottom pinched!'

'I might be so lucky Mr Spoilsport! I guess you're right though. I give in, but let's have some food first, I'm really hungry, and I think it's about time we had a glass of wine, don't you?'

'Your wish is my command,' he replies heading for the kitchen.

It's a couple of days later when, having taken Gianna out for her quick round-the-block morning walk, Rob returns looking shattered.

'Well so much for a quiet stroll,' he wheezes, unclipping Gianna's lead and collapsing on the sofa.

'Why, what happened?' I call from the kitchen.

'Well the traffic down there had piled up like a bowl of spaghetti so there was a gridlock and then a taxi driver who had clearly had enough decided to ride the pavement and nearly knocked us down in the process. Then I had to manoeuvre Gianna round a pile of abandoned pizza boxes and an empty catering-sized tin of tomatoes that had been left on the pavement by the restaurant round the corner. She put the brakes on and wrapped her mouth round a discarded crust before I could haul her out of the way. It's hardly surprising that she's overweight with so much temptation in her path.' At this he hauls himself up off the sofa and goes and stands at the window.

'Oh no, I don't believe it,' he cries, pressing his nose up against the glass and looking down into the street below.

'What's the problem?'

'Matey across the road is putting a string of Christmas lights round the door.'

'Let me see,' I laugh, joining Rob at the window.

Being four floors up we have to crane our necks to see what's going on below. 'Matey' or rather the attendant at the public loos, doesn't seem to get many customers, probably because the street is a really narrow rat-run for motorists trying to avoid the main roads of the city which are permanently clogged up with frustrated drivers.

'What puzzles me is why the authorities decided that this was a good place to position the conveniences in the first place

Chris. You rarely see a pedestrian because it's too bloomin' dangerous. You hardly ever see anyone making use of the facilities.'

'Matey' must have sensed our eyes on the back of his neck as he looks up at our window and gives us a morose glare. We pull away from the window and withdraw to the kitchen for breakfast. As soon as the plates come to the table Gianna is by our side with her chin resting on the table looking mournfully from one plate to the other.

'Do you remember how Eddie used to do this? It always makes me feel guilty,' says Rob biting into his pastry.

'Well just ignore her, don't give her eye-contact.'

'I'm trying not to but she just looks so appealing.'

'She's already had her breakfast and if you start feeding her at the table you'll live to regret it. You know it's something you should never do. She'll have to wait for her dinner this evening.'

'Why is it that she looks permanently miserable? It's a bit like beagles and Basset hounds, they never seem to smile like cockapoos do they? They always look cute and happy.'

'Yes and schnauzers look grumpy,' I laugh pouring another cup of coffee.

'And Newfies look daft and Afghans look snooty,' continues Rob. 'So what are we going to do with our day? And before you answer I refuse to do anything that involves climbing flights of stairs. I don't think my leg muscles could cope.'

'To be honest I just thought we could get the shopping done and then maybe take madam here for a W-A-L-K in the park. There's supposed to be a beautiful villa in there and there are views over the city and down to the river.'

'Sounds good to me.'

'Oh and please can we take Gianna into the supermarket this time? I'm dying to get a photo of her in one of the trolleys.'

'I suppose so, but how do you intend lifting 25 kilos of an overweight, low-slung dog into a trolley?'

'I'm sure we'd manage her between us if we took an end each,' I smile.

Unfortunately my idea isn't quite as simple as I'd imagined. When we get to the supermarket Gianna seems more than a little reluctant to be lifted and, as a result, tries every trick in the book to avoid being hoisted into the air. It's with one enormous joint effort that we eventually manage to get her into the trolley.

'Oh you have to admit, she does look cute Rob,' I laugh. 'It's a brilliant idea. Whoever thought of it was a genius. If only they'd introduce this in the UK. Think of the number of dogs we read about being stolen from outside shops.'

'Yes, you're right but I wouldn't want to be lifting anything heavier than Gianna. Come on then, let me take a photo of you both then we'd better get the shopping done.'

Having over-indulged in buying food and wine for Christmas the bags are really heavy and Gianna is proving to be a pain again. Trying to manoeuvre around other pedestrians with heavy bags and her pulling us in all directions except the one we want to go in is a nightmare. Then, to cap it all, she decides to repeat her trick of lying down, but fortunately this time she's on the pavement. A group of teenage girls stop to watch her antics and end up coming over to stroke her. Thinking she's in doggy heaven with all the attention, she rolls over onto her back and immediately ends up with several eager hands trying to rub her belly.

'*Ah! Lei è un tesoro!*' squeals one of the girls looking up at me. This dog is anything but a sweetheart in my opinion.

'*No! È una prima donna!*' I reply, leaning over and trying to heave Gianna back onto her feet. All I want to do is get home. The girls disperse and Gianna rolls back over onto her tummy and gets to her feet. 'Quick before she changes her mind!' I call to Rob who's clearly struggling with the shopping bags.

'You go on and I'll catch you up,' he shouts.

I have to almost drag Gianna back to the front door and bundle her into the lobby where we wait for Rob to appear. As the front door opens he arrives, laden down by the shopping bags and looking exhausted. We head for the lift and are only too pleased when it arrives quickly but, just as we're about to press the button, our sweaty friend in the football shirt turns up and squeezes his bulk in beside us, grunting. Unfortunately he's heading for our floor. By the time we get there the smell of garlic and sweat is overpowering and it's a huge relief when the doors open.

As I unload the shopping Rob sits himself down in one of the armchairs as Gianna has taken possession of the settee. 'That dog's going to be the death of me. My shoulder feels as though it's been wrenched out of its socket, my chest muscles are torn to shreds, my hands hurt. I'm sorry darling but would you mind horribly if we didn't go out this afternoon? I'm absolutely whacked.'

'No don't worry, but I'll have to take Gianna for a decent walk. You stay here and I'll take her out. And before you say anything, I'll be fine.'

It's a lovely afternoon and I decide to head for the Belvedere del Gianicolo in order to escape the bustle of the local area. Attaching Georgia's lead and grabbing my wooly hat and gloves I head out onto the landing and press the button for the lift. It seems to be taking an inordinately long time but I suppose there must be residents on the lower floors trying to call it too. Several minutes later there's still no sign of it arriving so I decide to walk down to the ground floor. Gianna's really keen to get moving and sets off down the stairs at a frighteningly fast pace, almost pulling me off my feet. I have to grab hold of the bannister and haul on the lead to stop her dragging me down head first. By the time we reach the bottom I'm physically shaking.

I notice a couple of women waiting outside the lift, one of them furiously pressing the button and overhear a torrent of abuse directed at the door. It seems as though the lift is *fuori servizio* again. I don't even want to think about the climb back up to the apartment if it isn't fixed by the time we get back.

Once I've managed to get Gianna past the mountains of rubbish that are now overflowing out of the communal bins and blocking our path, the streets become much more pleasant although graffiti still adorns every available wall, something that plagues Italy and that I've never truly understood. However, on entering the park I'm hugely disappointed to find the lawns neglected and the flower-beds full of weeds. This city seems to be on its knees. The one joy is the number of green parrots that are roosting in the trees, clearly very tame but horribly noisy. I sit down on a park bench and admire the view over the Tiber while Gianna follows her nose snuffling round the trees and flower-beds. The winter sun is bouncing off the dome of the Pantheon and I can also pick out the Basilica standing proud above the general sprawl of the city. The mountains form a stunning backdrop, the whole range now covered with snow. It seems such a pity that Rob isn't here to enjoy the view too. I'm quietly worrying about him and praying that his injuries aren't going to be too long-lasting.

'Come on then Gianna, let's get back home and see how Uncle Rob's doing. It's getting dark and he'll be wondering where we've got to,' I say, pulling her out of the park and back towards our street. I'm quietly praying that the problem with the lift was a temporary glitch but on entering the hallway my heart sinks when I see the sign stuck to the door. "*Questo ascensore sarà fuori servizio fino al 7 gennaio.*"

And so we begin the climb of the seventy-three stone steps. This is going to mean climbing up and down three times a day at least in order to get Gianna out. By the time we reach the final landing I've worked out that this will involve four hundred and thirty-eight steps a day minimum. I wonder how I'm going to break the news?

It's early the next morning, which is Christmas Eve, when I wander into the kitchen to make a coffee on the stove. Christmas music can be heard funnelling up between the buildings from the loos where Matey is now in full swing. There's suddenly what sounds like a loud groan coming from the bedroom.

'Are you alright in there?' I call.

'No,' comes the reply.

I head back to the bedroom to find Rob sitting on the side of the bed whimpering, his hands clutching the small of his back. 'What's the matter darling?' I ask, making my way round the end of the bed.

'I hate to say it love but I think I've damaged my back. It must have been trying to lift Gianna into the trolley yesterday and then carrying those heavy bags. I think I must have trapped a nerve or something because it's really, really painful.'

'Well let's get you back into bed and I'll prop you up on some pillows. Let me go and get you some pain-killers.' Fortunately we always carry a basic first aid kit so I'm able to get a couple of tablets down him immediately. However, on trying to lift Rob's head to add another pillow it's evident that he really has done himself a mischief as he cries out in pain.

'The problem is, sweetheart, that today's Christmas Eve and we won't be able to get you to a physio or an osteopath for at least three days. You're just going to have to rest.'

'But what about Gianna? You can't do all that walking on your own, she's too strong for you and as for the stairs. Oh Chris I feel dreadful about this.'

'Don't be silly, it can't be helped. I'll be fine. Just think how many calories I'll burn off. I'll be as fit as a fiddle by the time we leave. Anyhow, are we going to do things the Italian way and celebrate Christmas today or wait until tomorrow and be British?'

'Oh I think that it should be a case of when in Rome do as the Romans,' replies Rob with a weak smile. 'This hasn't exactly been a load of fun has it darling?' he says, taking my hand and looking forlornly up from his pillow.

'No, but it's been memorable, that's for sure. At least we'll be moving on in a few days. Crikey, which reminds me, I must send Gus and Rosa a text. Hang on a minute.' I return with Gianna who climbs up onto the bed and flops down next to Rob. 'Here, put these on and hang onto that,' I laugh, handing Rob a pair of antlers and an empty glass. 'I'll take a selfie for them. We need to look as though we're enjoying ourselves.'

'Do you know, in spite of everything I'm actually really fond of Gianna, she's a lovely dog,' he says, playing with her ears. 'But shouldn't I be raising a glass of Prosecco for this photo, I mean it is Christmas?'

'Not when you've just had two painkillers I'm afraid Mr Baird. It'll have to wait. So, are you ready you two? Say *famiglia*,' I laugh, holding up the phone ready for our selfie. '*Buon Natale!*'

BRIDGE OVER TROUBLED WATER

'WE REALLY DID STRIKE lucky didn't we Chris, I mean getting these two sits end to end?'

'Yes, it couldn't have worked out better could it?' I reply, staring out of the window at the passing scenery. 'I can't wait to see Venice again, it seems ages since we were last there.'

The city had always been a favourite with us, but staying in hotels or rental properties had always proved so expensive, but here we were, heading to a new sit where we could feel like residents instead of tourists.

'I do hope it's going to be okay, especially after our last experience, but even if it is a grotty house we've got the whole of Venice to explore.'

'Yes, and no dogs to walk, no stairs to climb, no early mornings, we can just sit back and watch the gondolas sailing past the window,' smiles Rob, leaning over and taking my hand.

'Alright Casanova, but let's not get too excited before we've seen what we've let ourselves in for.'

I was actually feeling quite confident about our new adventure. Having chatted to the owners, Francesca and Mario on FaceTime and made a point of looking carefully at the room they were sitting in, I reckoned we'd landed on our feet this time. The décor seemed very tasteful and the place looked clean, and what we were really excited about was the fact that the apartment was on the ground floor of a house that was actually on the Grand Canal. Our charges were to be two kittens, cutely named Dante and Beatrice, that had been found in a bag on one of the boats where residents leave their rubbish. It all seemed too good to be true.

'Look Rob!' I say excitedly, pointing through the window, 'we're crossing the lagoon!' I've never tired of the magical experience of arriving in the city and today was no exception. 'Oh the light is perfect, isn't it wonderful?'

As the train pulls into Santa Lucia and everyone starts collecting their belongings I can feel the excitement building inside me. I've seen the view from the steps of the station so many times but it never disappoints. It's as though we're leaving the real world behind and walking onto a film set.

'You're like a little girl in a sweet shop aren't you?' remarks Rob laughing and helping me with my case.

'I know, I don't know what it is about Venice that gets to me but it always makes me feel so emotional,' I smile.

'Come on then Mrs Baird, let's see if we can find our way to our new abode only stay close to me or you may never see me again!'

It's some 45 minutes later that we step off the *vaporetto* at the Accademia bridge, the stop nearest to our accommodation, the journey down the Grand Canal in the water-bus familiar, but as spellbinding as ever. Fortunately I'm blessed with a good sense of direction and it's only a matter of minutes before we arrive at the end of a narrow, blind alley which, I feel confident, is where we need to be.

'I reckon this is us,' I say, turning to Rob and heading down to the end of the passage-way where we find a door with several doorbells and names on a brass plaque. It's only then that I realise that we've been followed by a couple who, I assume, must live in the same apartments. 'I'm sorry, do let me get out of your way, we've just arrived,' I apologise.

'Oh no, we don't live here,' replies the woman in a strong Australian accent, 'only we thought this gentleman was that famous American actor and we were following you, I'm so sorry.' And with that the couple, looking somewhat embarrassed, turn and walk quickly back up the alley and out of sight.

'Well that was interesting darling,' says Rob, with a smug look on his face. 'I wonder who they thought I was?'

'I reckon it was the Borsalino and the new beard that did it,' I reply looking more studiously at Rob's face. 'Anyhow, let's ring the bell and hope that we've got the right place.'

The door is answered by a rather large man, probably in his fifties, with very little hair, who's wearing a pair of very small but stylish spectacles on the end of a rather squashed nose. He's dressed in a smart pair of trousers and what looks like a cashmere sweater in a striking shade of purple.

'*Buona sera! Ah, Christina and Roberto!*' he says, smiling warmly and holding out his hand in greeting. 'Plees to come in,' he says dramatically, bowing with a flourish. 'Plees to follow me,' and he leads us into a dimly-lit, panelled hallway surrounded by several very small, dark, wooden doors. '*Francesca,*' he shouts, opening one of the doors and ducking to enter, '*Christina e Roberto sono arrivati.*'

The doors are so small that one can only assume that the Venetians used to be a very small race, as even I have to duck to enter. An elderly woman appears from one of the doorways, her black dress merging with the shadows. She's tall and elegant but appears to be somewhat older than Mario. Her short, grey hair frames a long, ovoid face and her long neck reminds me of a Modigliani painting.

'*Buona sera e benvenuti a Venezia,*' she smiles taking Rob's hand in hers and stroking his arm before greeting me with a kiss on each cheek. '*Siamo così felici di incontrarvi finalmente.* Plees you must come in.'

I'm quietly relieved to hear a few words in English as with my limited Italian I'd be struggling to conduct our entire meeting in what currently feels like a very foreign language. I manage to thank her and walk through into the sitting-room.

I'm immediately in love with the apartment, the room is surprisingly cosy and furnished with typical Venetian decor. At one end stands a beautiful, ornate, stone fireplace decorated with scrolled carvings; a corner cabinet displays a collection of Murano glass and walls that are adorned with what appear to be original oil paintings of the city.

'*Complimenti, avete un appartamento bellissimo!*' I say, turning to our hosts. It's only then that I notice the view from the two small windows — the Grand Canal! I can't contain my excitement. 'Oh my, this is amazing! A view of the Grand Canal from the window Rob. Come and look!'

As Rob walks over to admire the view I can hear a tiny meow coming from behind the settee and out pads the cutest little ginger kitten. Francesca runs over and scoops him up. '*Questo è Dante,*' she says, holding him proudly aloft. '*È il mio bambino ma è molto birichino,*' she says, rubbing her nose against his and laughing. '*Ecco Christina,*' she says, handing him over to me. It's a very long time since I've held something so small and so adorable.

'Oh he's gorgeous. I love him already!' I croon and pretend to put him inside my coat and smuggle him out making Mario laugh. '*È adorabile! E dove Beatrice?*' I ask, looking around in search of his sister.

'*Seguimi,*' she replies, beckoning me through to another room. She opens the door quietly and there, snuggled up on the bed, is a pretty, tortoiseshell kitten. She's sound asleep but when Francesca reaches over to pick her up a pair of huge, blue eyes appear in her tiny face and she makes a loud miaow in protest at being woken up.

'*Quanti anni hanno?*' I ask.

'*Sei settimane,*' she replies.

Only six weeks, how could anyone have wanted to get rid of the poor little mites? They're so innocent and vulnerable.

'They are to stay in the house because of canals,' says

Francesca, leading me back to the sitting-room, Beatrice in her hands. 'Roberto you have *il mio tesorino*,' she says, handing the kitten to Rob. I can see that he's instantly besotted as Beatrice opens her mouth wide and cries out before trying to climb up his sweater.

'So please you give me your coat,' says Mario, beginning to take Rob's coat from his shoulders while Rob juggles Beatrice between his hands. 'You like a drink? Negroni? Spritz?'

'A spritz would be lovely thank you Mario,' replies Rob, slipping his arms out of his coat, at which point Beatrice springs from his hands and lands on the back of an armchair where she settles herself.

'And Christina?' asks Mario turning to me.

'Yes, a spritz for me too please Mario,' I reply.

Rob has wandered back to the window and is staring out at the magic that is Venice. It's already dark but the lights from the nearby buildings reflect on the water. A *vaporetto* chugs by heading for St Mark's, followed by a couple of water taxis, their passengers standing with their heads sticking out of the top of the boat, their phones clicking away madly. I drape my coat over one of the chairs and walk over to join Rob at the window.

'I think we've hit the jackpot my darling,' he whispers. 'It's wonderful, absolutely wonderful.'

With Mario and Francesca departed the next day to visit friends in Rome (about which we are tactfully polite) we leave the kittens in the kitchen, clad ourselves in our winter coats and head off to find a supermarket, Rob sporting his Borsalino.

'I wonder who that couple thought I was?' he asks as we head towards the end of the alley. 'They did say an American actor didn't they? It was probably George Clooney, he got married here didn't he?'

'Yes but I doubt very much that they were thinking George Clooney. It was more likely to be Denzel Washington.'

'Denzel Washington? But he's black!'

'I know but it was getting dark. Or maybe it was Kirk Douglas?'

'But he's dead!'

'Oh. What about Jack Nicholson?' I suggest, taking Rob's arm and steering him round a corner.

'Now you're just trying to wind me up. I'm sticking with George Clooney,' he replies, giving his hat a tweak. 'And how is it you always seem to know where we're going? I wouldn't have a clue.'

'But we've used the supermarket on the Zattere lots of times, you must remember how to get there by now?'

'Nope. Not a clue. I'm totally lost already. All the bridges look the same to me and I can't tell one canal from the other.'

My husband's ability to get lost never fails to amuse me (and frequently to worry me). He seems to have no sense of direction and maps mean absolutely nothing to him. I have to resort to writing down detailed instructions as to how to get from A to B if we're unable to travel together.

It's only a few minutes before we reach the wide expanse of the Giudecca Canal. It's surprisingly quiet and the winter sun casts the most wonderful light on the buildings.

'It's bliss not to have any traffic isn't it Chris? It just seems to slow the whole pace of life down several notches and it's so much quieter at this time of year.'

'Yes, I'd much rather come in the winter without the crowds and the heat. It's no fun trying to fight your way down those narrow alleys when it's heaving,' I reply.

The cafes that line the water-front along the Zattere are busy and there's the usual queue at Nico's, the ice-cream shop. I can see Rob looking longingly at the people who are leaving the *gelateria*, ice-cream in hand.

'Not today Mr Baird, we've got shopping to do.'

'Oh but look at that Chris! It looks delicious,' he says, turning and watching a young boy mounting an attack on a cone piled high with chocolate ice-cream.

'We've got plenty of time for ice-creams, what we need are groceries.'

'And wine I hope?'

'Yes, and wine.'

We return to the apartment with our shopping bags loaded with food, a bottle of red wine and a bottle of Prosecco. The kittens are pleased to see us and have somehow managed to get up on the kitchen counter so are pouncing on the shopping as we unload everything.

'We'd better remember not to leave anything on the top here or they'll make a real mess and eat everything. Do you remember when Charlie ate all the Parmesan cheese?'

Charlie was the very first cat that we looked after and was also the first feline to win Rob's heart. Sadly he had become one of the many animals that we'd cared for that had since died, a sweet-tempered, gentle soul.

'Oh yes, dear little Charlie. He was a lovely fellow, but I have to say these two are rather gorgeous,' replies Rob, as Dante disappears inside one of the carrier bags. 'He's a cutie isn't he? He's so funny when he plays.'

Being preoccupied with unloading the shopping I haven't paid attention to the whereabouts of Beatrice. 'Where's his sister Rob? I didn't notice her walk out of here.'

'I'll go and look, she can't be far away.'

It's some minutes later when a rather irate Rob returns to the kitchen holding out his favourite cashmere sweater. 'Look at this!' he snaps, holding it up for me to inspect. 'It's ruined!'

'Why? What's happened to it?'

'Beatrice had climbed into my suitcase and was curled up on top of it and dribbling everywhere. She's pulled at the wool and slobbered all over it and now it's all snagged and soggy.'

I know how fond Rob is of his cashmere and this particular jumper was his favourite; a soft, grey, polo-neck that he'd coveted for some time before deciding to treat himself. It hadn't come cheap.

'Yikes, it is a bit of a mess isn't it?' I say, examining the damage. 'I'll see if I can sort those snags out and the dribble will wash out, don't worry. I trust that you've moved your suitcase?'

'Yes, I've put it under the bed and zipped it up.'

'And I trust you haven't left anything else around that our dear little friends can ruin?'

'No, everything's out of reach. I've made sure of that.'

'So what are we going to do with our day? It's so lovely out there we really ought to get out and explore.'

'Fine by me,' replies Rob. 'Maybe we could treat ourselves to lunch somewhere?'

'*Perfetto!*' I smile and head for the bedroom to get my coat.

It's late afternoon by the time we return, pleasantly weary and a little tipsy having drunk rather a lot of wine over lunch. Being in Venice I couldn't resist the seafood and I'd taken the advice of the waiter and decided to try a bit of everything from the list of starters on the menu. I'd made my way through fried squid, sardines with onions, a pasta with clams and a portion of fish stew with prawns before heading straight for the tiramisu. Even Rob had been adventurous and eaten a beef carpaccio as well as liver, something I can never persuade him to eat at home but a speciality in Venice.

The kittens make a fuss of us as we settle down in the armchairs to watch the traffic on the water, Dante climbing all over Rob and 'wowing' in his ear before settling down on his shoulder. Beatrice makes her way onto my lap and quickly falls asleep.

A huge array of traffic passes the window, a reminder that everything in the city happens on the water, from deliveries to the essential services dealing with accidents or illness. An ambulance skims the water heading for the short-cut to the hospital at the north of the city while a boat full of water bottles and wine moors up outside a nearby hotel. As the light begins to fade a flotilla of gondolas sails past, the boats full of Japanese tourists being serenaded by a portly Italian who is standing up, arms held aloft as he sings *Volare*. He's being accompanied by an accordion, played by an equally large man wearing a traditional striped *gondolieri* jumper. It all seems quite magical, like a theatre outside our window, and as Rob starts snoring I can feel my eyes getting heavier.

It's pitch dark when I wake up, but on heading for the kitchen I'm suddenly overtaken by a wave of nausea. Realising that I'm going to throw up I head quickly for the bathroom where I'm horribly sick. It's only then that I realise that I've been foolish enough to eat seafood, something which has, on several occasions, disagreed with me, two of those occasions being here in Venice. I know that I have an intolerance to mussels so always avoid them, but if an item of fish has so much as been sitting next to a mussel in the restaurant kitchen I can become really quite poorly. It may have been the sea food stew, or the *vongole*, who knows, but whatever it was I think I might be in the bathroom for some time.

It's about half an hour before Rob wakes up, discovers that I'm missing and knocks on the bathroom door.

'Are you alright in there?'

'No,' I cry, preparing to wretch for the umpteenth time. 'I think I've had an allergic reaction to the seafood.'

'Oh my poor love, how awful. What can I do?'

'Nothing I'm afraid, I'll just have to ride the storm,' I reply, opening the bathroom door.

'Blimey, you're a pretty awful colour Chris,' he comments on seeing my face. 'Maybe you should go and lie down?'

'I don't think I should yet, my stomach's still heaving and I'm sweating. I think I'd better stay here for a while if you don't mind.'

It must be about seven the following morning when I eventually wake up having crashed out early after my bout of sickness, but I'm feeling extremely weak and wobbly and the feeling of nausea is still lingering. 'I'm sorry love but I really don't think I can cope with being vertical just yet,' I say apologetically.

'It's alright sweetheart, I just feel so rotten for you and so helpless.'

'Well actually you could help Rob. The rubbish has to be taken to the boat before eight o'clock and it'll have to go or the cat litter will stink the place out. It's already quarter to.'

'Oh, alright, I'm sure I can manage that. So where exactly does it have to go?'

'To the boat in the Campo according to Mario's instructions. You can't really miss it, it's just at the end of our street.'

'Okay. So is that right or left at the end of our alley?'

'Right, then over the second bridge you come to and the boat will be there on the left. You can't miss it, it'll be piled with rubbish.'

'I'd better get on with it then. Are you sure you'll be alright on your own?' he asks, throwing on some clothes.

'Yes, fine. I think I just need to sleep. I'm sorry to be such a bore.'

'Don't you worry, I'll pop out now and get it done and I'll be straight back.'

The trouble is I do worry. Letting Rob out on his own in somewhere as confusing as Venice is not a good idea. As I turn over and pull the covers over me I can't help but fret.

I don't remember falling asleep again but wake with a start and grab my watch off the bedside table. It's quarter past nine. Dante and Beatrice are both curled up beside me but there's no sign of Rob.

'Darling,' I call through to the sitting-room. There's no reply. 'Ro-ob?' I shout. Still no reply. I climb gingerly out of bed, waking the kittens as I pull back the covers and walk hesitantly through to the sitting-room. There's no sign of him. I head back to the bedroom to get my phone, pressing my hands against the walls to steady myself, my legs feeling decidedly wobbly. I ring his number only to be told that the phone is switched to voicemail. I despair. He's obviously got lost. Surely he would have the sense to ring me if he'd lost his way but then again, perhaps not. I've teased him so many times about his ability to get lost in a phone-box that his pride wouldn't let him. Did he even have the address with him? I doubt it as he was only supposed to be going to the end of the street and anyhow, addresses in Venice are notoriously difficult to find as the numbers don't necessarily follow a sequence. It's easier to say "three doors along from the *pasticceria* in such-and-such a street," but even that would tax Rob.

By half-past nine there's still no sign of him and I'm becoming seriously worried. Dante is patting me gently in the face with his paw and Beatrice is sitting on my head. It's only then that I realise that they haven't been fed poor things so, steadying myself against the wall I climb out of bed and head for the kitchen.

It's while I'm feeding the kittens that I become aware of voices coming from the canal-side of the apartment. Curious to know what's going on I make my way slowly towards the window and, as I do so, am convinced that I can here Rob's voice. Opening the window and leaning out over the water my suspicions are confirmed as, who should be standing on next door's landing-stage, laughing and waving his arms around Italian-style, but Rob. Leaning back seductively over the wooden framework that surrounds the platform is a curvaceous red-head who's tossing her locks flirtatiously over her shoulders while smoking a cigarette. She's probably in her late fifties and is dressed in a figure-hugging, red dress with a low neckline which reveals a rather garish necklace that she keeps fiddling with, displaying her long, painted nails.

'*Si, si Roberto* eet eesa true, but what eesa your wife saying?' she laughs coquettishly in a low, dusky voice, taking a drag on her cigarette and winking at him provocatively.

'His wife is saying that she's been worried sick about him for the last hour and would appreciate it if he could cut short his little rendezvous and come back to look after her!' I shout, trying to make myself heard above the noise of a passing launch.

'Oh, hello darling,' says Rob, turning in my direction. 'Er, this is our neighbour Sofia, she invited me in for a drink.'

On noticing the glass in his hand for the first time I slam the window shut, flounce back to bed and turn over with my back to the door. I can hear the key turning in the lock but lie still, my head buried in the pillow. The outer door closes quietly and I can hear Rob approaching. Opening the bedroom door he comes and sits down on the edge of the bed.

'Hello darling, how are you feeling?' he says gently, attempting to peel back the cover.

I snatch it back and ignore him as I'm still trying to contain my fury.

'Oh come on, I was only next door. I met Sofia at the boat and it was only when we headed down the alleyway that we realised we were neighbours. She invited me to go and see her apartment and then next thing I knew she was handing me a cognac. I could hardly refuse now could I?'

Feeling absolutely incensed I sit bolt upright and glare at him. 'No, I'm sure you couldn't possibly leave your glamorous new friend to come and look after your poor, sick wife. Do you realise how long you've been gone? An hour and three-quarters! I've been worried sick about you. Why didn't you ring me or knock on the door to let me know where you were?' I wail, throwing myself back down onto the pillow and reaching for a tissue.

'Well for one thing I'd left my phone here in my jacket pocket and I didn't think it would be more than a quick visit to be polite. It's a really weird apartment. It's been done up as though you're on a boat but it's all been decorated in the most ghastly shade of green, a bit like being under water, and it's all done in Murano glass, even the bedroom.'

'The bedroom?' I scream sitting bolt upright again. 'What might I ask were you doing in her bedroom?'

'I wasn't actually *in* the bedroom. It isn't a separate room because the apartment's just one long open space so I didn't go *into* the bedroom but I could see the layout from the kitchen. Anyhow, can I get you anything darling?'

'No,' is my sharp reply throwing myself back down on the pillow. 'I just want to sleep.'

'Well okay, I'll leave you alone, but give me a shout if you want anything.'

By early evening I'm still feeling under the weather so have to accept that Rob is going to have to venture out and do the shopping. Quite how he's going to find his way to the supermarket without tying a ball of string to the doorknob is beyond me. I'm beginning to feel somewhat put out that our stay in Venice is being spoiled by my being poorly when all I want is to be out there enjoying the city.

'Don't worry, I promise not to be long and if our neighbour appears I shall refuse any invitations and be straight home,' Rob promises.

'Are you sure you know where you're going?' I ask weakly. 'It's dark out there already.'

'Absolutely. Up the alley, turn right, turn left before the bridge in the campo, up to the Guidecca turn right and straight along the Zattere to the supermarket.'

I'm actually quite taken aback that he seems to know where he's going for once.

'Phone?' I hint.

'In my pocket and yes, it is switched on. I'll see you soon sweetheart. Just take it easy and hopefully you'll be feeling stronger by the time I get back.'

I drift in and out of sleep, the kittens snuggled up against me purring rhythmically. I can hear the gondoliers serenading the tourists in the distance as their flotilla turns outside our window. I'm unsure of the time but already worrying about Rob and his sense of direction. He's managed to get lost so many times that I always anticipate having to go looking for him but trying to find a missing person in this city would prove more than a challenge. It's just as I begin to reach for my phone that I hear the front door open and breathe a sigh of relief.

'You okay?' I call out.

'No I am not,' comes the terse reply.

'Why? Was there a problem? I hope you didn't get lost?'

'No, I knew exactly where I was going but no-one happened to mention that there was going to be an *aqua alta* this evening,' comes a less than happy voice from the hallway. I can hear him muttering to himself and it's a few moments before he appears in the bedroom, red-faced with his trousers rolled up to his knees and holding his shoes aloft. I have to try hard to suppress a laugh.

'My best brogues are ruined Chris,' he wails, 'ruined. And as for these cords I don't know how they'll survive. They're absolutely soaked.'

'Oh darling I'm sorry. I had no idea there was going to be a high tide. I would never have suggested that you went shopping if I'd known. Why don't you take your trousers off and we'll see what we can do. If you stuff some newspaper in your shoes it'll help to dry them out.'

My man is far from happy. I drag myself out of bed and throw a sweater on over my pyjamas before heading for the bathroom.

'I've probably caught Weil disease as well. I actually saw a rat swimming along the wall under the bridge in the Campo,' comes the cry from the bedroom.

'Sweetheart I doubt very much that you'll have caught anything. You've only been paddling, not swimming. Anyhow, let me have your cords and I'll put them straight in the washing-machine and then maybe we could have something to eat? Did you get anything nice?'

'I got some risotto, I thought it might help to settle your stomach. Oh, and I bought you a little present.'

'Oh that was thoughtful of you, what is it?'

'Here,' he says delving into his coat pocket and handing me a small package. 'I hope you like it. And I'm sorry about this morning.'

I peel back the seal from the paper and remove the contents, something wrapped in tissue paper.

'Be careful, it's fragile,' says Rob, hovering over me.

I fold back the tissue to reveal two tiny cats made of glass, one ginger and one tortoiseshell.

'Oh Rob, they're absolutely beautiful. Thank you so much,' I say, choking back the tears. 'I'm sorry if I was so prickly this morning but I was feeling so lousy. Anyhow, thank you, it's really sweet of you.'

'And I'm sorry too. I just thought they'd be a nice memento of our stay,' he replies. 'And where are the terrible two?'

'I've no idea, they were in the bedroom with me. They're probably up to no good, I guess we'd better find them.'

It's on entering the bathroom that I find both of them sitting on the floor, transfixed by the action of the washing-machine where Rob's cords are revolving in the drum. Dante is sitting up with his front paws in the air his head following the rotation of the washing.

'They're so cute Rob. It would be lovely to have a cat don't you think?'

'You know my feelings on that subject Chris. I'd be worried sick about them getting knocked over or savaged and I don't want a cat chasing the birds away or, even worse, killing one. No, I think we'll just stick to looking after other people's. Anyhow, are you up for a glass of something yet?'

'Maybe a very small glass of wine but purely medicinal. Thank you. And speaking of wine, have we got anything for tomorrow evening or had you forgotten that it's New Year's Eve?'

'No I hadn't forgotten and there are two small bottles of Bellini in the fridge already. Let's hope you're firing on all cylinders by then.'

The next morning is blissfully sunny so we decide to head out for a gentle stroll.

'Maybe we could just jump on the *vaporetto* and travel up the Grand Canal?' I suggest. 'I'm still a bit weak so it would be nice to sit back and see everything from the water.'

'Good idea. I'll go and get my things,' replies Rob heading for the bedroom. However, it isn't long before he returns with a puzzled look on his face.

'Have you lost something?' I ask as he heads off to the sitting room and starts searching behind cushions.

'Yes, my Borsalino. I could have sworn I put it on top of the wardrobe but it isn't there now.'

'Are you sure that's where you put it? You were in a bit of a state when you got back so maybe you put it down somewhere else?'

'No, I definitely put it back up there so the kittens couldn't get at it.'

'Let me go and have a look,' I reply and head off down the corridor to the bedroom. No, he's right. There's no sign of his hat. It's just as I'm leaving the room that I hear a loud meow coming from under the bed. Dropping down on all fours to see what's going on, who should I spy but Dante and Beatrice batting Rob's hat backwards and forwards and pouncing on the crown. I manage to squeeze under the bed frame and grab the brim but at the same time Dante digs his claws into the felt and skids across the floor still attached to the hat. Alerted by the noise Rob appears at the door just as I manage to recover his Borsalino with Dante still attached.

'What on earth are you …? Is that my hat? How on earth did it get down there?'

'I'd guess that one of these two managed to scale the wardrobe and knock it down.'

'But how? They couldn't have climbed up a vertical wooden face?'

'I have a horrible feeling that they might have scaled up your coat. You'd left it on a hanger so it would have made an ideal climbing post.'

'I don't believe it. You mean to say that one of these monsters managed to get up there and knock it down? I hope it's not damaged?'

'No just a bit dusty, it'll soon brush off. Let's put these two in the kitchen and get moving.'

The light is just beginning to fade when we return home, our supposed short outing having turned into a major day's hike. Having travelled as far as the railway station on the *vaporetto* we'd decided to find our way back on foot through the labyrinth of small streets in Santa Croce and San Polo before eventually arriving in the more familiar territory of Dorsoduro. By the time we get back our feet are aching and we're both feeling exhausted.

'I don't know how you do it Chris, you're a miracle. How on earth did you know the way back? I was totally and utterly lost.'

'I guess I'm just lucky in having a built-in sense of direction but I have to admit there was more than a bit of guess-work involved. It doesn't matter how many times we come here I always get confused at some point.'

'Well I reckon we've seen every glass shop and mask shop north of the Grand Canal!'

'South,' I correct him, laughing. 'We're on the south of the city.'

'I keep meaning to say that we don't see as many cats around these days. Do you remember when we first started coming here there'd always be plenty of them lying around the streets and campos and little saucers of left-over pasta that the locals left for them? I wonder what's happened to them?'

'I think there was a campaign to clear the place up and a major effort to neuter or sterilise them. A lot of them were sick too so it was probably the best thing to do under the circumstances.'

'But surely they must have helped to keep the rats under control?'

'I'm sure that was why they were left to their own devices for so long, but the numbers are way down on what they used to be, a bit like the local population.'

'I suppose you're right but you can understand why people leave. Apart from it being so damned expensive, who wants to be living somewhere that's heaving with tourists all the time?'

'You mean people like us?'

'Well, yes, I suppose so. But I don't feel like a tourist this time, I feel like a resident and I love it!' says Rob wandering over to the window.

We're suddenly interrupted by a loud bang which sends Dante and Beatrice fleeing to the bedroom.

'Fireworks! They're starting early. We're going to have to keep the kittens in the back room, Rob. We're so close to St Mark's here that there's going to be a lot of noise.'

106

There's immediately another bang and a huge ball of light explodes in the distant sky like a huge dandelion clock. It isn't yet dark enough to admire the display but it's a taste of what's to follow later in the evening.

'It's a pity we can't go and join in the celebrations,' says Rob, waving to a boat-load of Japanese visitors, 'but I agree, we need to stay put for the kittens, they're bound to be frightened. I wish someone would ban fireworks altogether or at least make some that don't go bang. The distress they cause the animals is dreadful. Do you remember how Holly used to literally climb the walls?'

'Yes I do. It was awful to have to watch her bless her.' Our own border terrier suffered terribly from loud noises and would tremble for hours after the event. We'd tried medication and calming pheromones, but nothing seemed to help her. It was only when she became deaf that she coped with the noise. 'To be honest I'd rather stay in. I was in St Mark's for New Year on my own many years ago and it was terrifying.'

'Terrifying? Why was that? Were you being groped by lusty Italians?' asks Rob, settling down in one of the arm-chairs by the window.

'No, it was the fireworks that were frightening. People were letting off cheap fire-crackers that had come in from China and they were shooting across the Piazza at ground level. The ones that did head upwards were landing on the roof-tops around St Mark's. I'm surprised there wasn't a fire. And the sad thing I remember was a young couple who were standing right in front of me had a falling-out and decided to go their separate ways. They just dropped hands, turned their backs on each other and walked off in opposite directions. I've never forgotten it.'

'So much for romance! Anyhow, do you want to have a shower before we have dinner?'

'Good idea, I could do with freshening up after that walk. I won't be long.'

The bathroom and the bedroom both smell a bit musty, but that's the nature of Venice. Unfortunately due to the recent high water the bathroom's smelling a bit honky too so I don't linger too long. I change into my smartest outfit as a gesture to the occasion and head back to the sitting-room, only to find Rob lying flat out on the floor and heading towards me on all fours.

'What on earth are you doing?' I ask pausing in my tracks. 'I assume you're playing some sort of game with the kittens or have you dropped something on the floor?'

'No!' he replies in a loud whisper. 'It's Sofia, she's outside on her balcony and she keeps looking this way. I don't want her to see me.'

'Why ever not? Are you afraid she's going to pounce again?'

'No but she might invite us round for a New Year's drink or something.'

'Well we have the perfect excuse to say no. We've got to stay put to look after the kittens.'

'I suppose you're right,' replies Rob, grabbing hold of the arm of one of the chairs and hauling himself up off the floor. 'I hadn't thought of that. Anyhow, I'd better go and make myself look even more dashing than usual for you,' he says, heading for the bathroom. 'I need to give my beard a trim just in case I get mistaken for that handsome American actor again.'

By eleven o'clock the noise from the Piazza is drifting in our direction and the occasional firework lights up the sky over the Grand Canal. I can't resist opening the window and looking up towards the expanse of water outside St Mark's. The gondolas are still in business and the usual flotilla of tourists comes sailing past, one so close that we could almost touch hands. The tenor begins to serenade his passengers with his usual rendition of *Volare* and gives a friendly wave as the boats turn in order to head back to St Mark's. Rob appears with two Bellinis and we raise our glasses to the people in the gondolas. I realise that they must think we live in the house and it actually feels as though we do.

'It's the wonderful thing about house-sitting isn't it Rob? You never feel like a tourist, you feel part of a community. I mean all those folk in the gondolas are obviously having a wonderful time but they're probably paying a fortune to stay in a hotel and here we are living for free with front row seats on the Grand Canal itself. We're so very lucky,' I muse, staring dreamily into the water.

Unfortunately, my attention having wandered, I've failed to notice the appearance of our neighbour who has slunk out of the shadows of her apartment and onto her landing-stage. She's holding a champagne flute in one hand and, raising the other, waggles her fingers in Rob's direction and calls out, '*Ciao Roberto!*'

Looking suitably embarrassed Rob waves weakly back and returns her greeting, '*Ciao Sofia!* Er, this is my wife Christine,' he announces, quickly putting his arm around my shoulder.

'*Buonasera Signora*,' she replies giving me a little wave. I wave limply back. 'You, er, you like a leetl drink in my house plees?' she asks.

She's already tottering dangerously on the wooden platform in a pair of six-inch stilettos, her hand occasionally reaching out to the wooden framework to steady herself. In spite of the fact that it's the last day of December and decidedly cold, her extremely short dress leaves very little to the imagination. The plunging neckline is adorned with large sequins and unfortunately the design is such that they emphasise her already generous cleavage. A pair of enormous diamanté earrings reach almost to her shoulders, and a matching choker is clasped tightly around her neck. It's only when she turns towards the light that is radiating from our window that I notice that she's only got make-up on one of her eyes which does little to enhance her already rather drunken appearance. Whether she put her make-up on before or after hitting the bottle is difficult to tell. The result resembles a drag-queen who's been disturbed in the dressing-room before being able to put the final touches to their appearance.

I'm much relieved that we have the excuse of the cats to escape having to spend any more time with her. '*Grazie Signora ma dobbiamo restare qui. I gattini hanno paura dei fuochi d'artificio,*' I reply, hoping I've managed to navigate my way through the sentence.

A strong evening breeze is beginning to cause the surface of the canal to get a bit choppy so that the passing traffic causes a swell to wash up against the wall of our apartment and, occasionally, splashes onto Sofia's landing-stage. She seems blissfully unaware but keeps topping up her glass. She doesn't seem too upset by my turning down the invitation and so, with a wave and a '*Buon Capodanno*' we close the window and retreat into the sitting-room.

'Well that was lucky,' sighs Rob taking a sip from his glass. 'I do hope she's going to be alright out there. She seemed rather unsteady on her feet.'

'It might help if she took her stilettos off and stopped drinking. She's already well away and it isn't even midnight yet. Anyhow, I think we ought to head for the bedroom and take these two tigers with us. If we put some music on it'll help to drown out the fireworks.'

'Okay boss. I've got the bottles. After you.'

We stretch ourselves out on the bed, propped up on the pillows, Dante and Beatrice tucked in between us, Beatrice hugging Dante and chewing his tail.

It's almost midnight when my phone shows that there's a new message from Mario and Francesca.

'So what does it say?' asks Rob, leaning over to try and read the text.

'It's a photo of them both wearing "I love Rome" t-shirts and raising a glass with "*Buon Capodanno!*" written in the message.

'Oh that's nice of them and I'm glad somebody likes Rome. Still, each to his own, I don't know how anyone could fail to fall in love with this place,' he ponders. 'Do you know who it was who said, "Venice is the most romantic place in the world but it's even better when there is no one around?"'

'Not a clue, but I'm sure you're going to tell me.'

'Woody Allen, and do you know what my darling?'

'What?' I ask suspiciously.

'He was right. Happy New Year sweetheart. I'm glad it's just us.'

THE WATERS OF TYNE

'THERE'S A COUPLE HERE, Maureen and Jackie, wanting someone to look after their Old English sheepdog for a couple of weeks, Rob,' I hint, having searched the website for a new housesit.

'Whereabouts?' comes a somewhat bored response from behind the newspaper where Rob's still struggling with the Sudoku.

'Just north of Newcastle, in Whitley Bay,' I reply. 'That's on the coast so it would be bang next to the sea.'

'Sounds okay, but what's the accommodation?'

'According to the blurb it's "a 1930s three-bedroomed, two-bathroomed house overlooking the front, with a large garden, close to all local amenities and within easy reach of the Metro. Kevin will need two good walks a day but there are plenty close to the house."'

'Kevin? You did say Kevin? Who on earth calls a dog Kevin?'

'Well clearly these two. There must be a good reason for it. Anyhow, what do you think? I've always fancied a Dulux dog. It used to be my dream to live in York and have a bicycle and an Old English sheepdog.'

'Well it's better than sitting here looking at the rain. By all means give it a go. But out of interest, how old is Kevin?'

'Er, let me have a look. He's ten months old so he should have had some training by the time the sit starts.'

'Well it's okay by me. I think we could both do with a change of scenery and it's new territory for me.'

'It's only a few miles south of all those wonderful coastal paths in Northumberland that we've seen on the television. We could probably get there by train and there'd be some great walks for the dog.'

'Well get on with it, PA, what are you waiting for?' orders Rob returning to his puzzle.

'Aa'reet pet, come on in,' invites our host. 'You must be Christine. Divn't just stand there hinny! Aw and you must be Rob, pleased to meet you!' he says warmly. 'Ha'way in and take a pew, you must be knackered the pair of you. Go on, sit yersels doon. Can I get you summat to drink?'

'A cup of tea would be lovely, thank you, Jackie,' I reply, taking a seat.

'And what about you Rob? Would you like a cuppa or something a bit stronger? I've got some Newky Broon if you fancy one.'

'Er, no thanks, a cup of tea would be fine,' replies Rob looking a little confused.

'Aareet, I'll put the kettle on if you're shooa that's arl ye want. So weor d'yer come from Rob?' asks our host, heading into the utility room.

'What did he say?' whispers Rob hurriedly.

'He's asking you where you come from,' I laugh.

'Oh, originally from Scotland,' calls Rob.

'Ah thort ah picked up a slight accent,' comes the voice. 'Whereaboots?'

'Edinburgh,' replies Rob.

'Aah so yer a Jock are ye? But Edinburgh's a bit posh isn't it? A mean ye haven't got much of an accent. How long have ye been away from yem?'

Rob looks at me again, his scrunched-up expression indicating that he needs help.

'He's asking you how long you've been away from home,' I reply in a loud whisper.

'Oh, about forty years I guess,' Rob shouts.

'Why that's a long time te be away. Ah divvent think ah could ever move away from heor, ah love it too much ye naa,' says our host, returning to the kitchen carrying two large, steaming mugs of tea to the table. Builders' tea would look weak by comparison.

'Thank you Jackie, that's just what I need, it's been a long day,' I remark, quietly wondering how I'm going to get the startlingly orange brew down me.

'Owa Maureen's oot with Kevin just now but she should be back soon. Mind you it's propa clarty oot on the fields at the moment, we've had so much rain but you're welcome to borrow owa wellies if you want.'

'Kevin's a great name for a dog Jackie. Where did he get that from?' asks Rob, looking up from his mug.

'Aw ees named afta Kevin Keegan, Rob. Ees ded good with a football too, he'll like it if you kick a ball for 'im. Needless to say I'm a big Newcastle supporter. Me Dad named me after Jackie Milburn and we called owa lad Malcolm after Malcolm McDonald. Neva miss a game if ah can help it. So which team do you support Rob? I guess it's Hibernian if you're from Edinburgh?'

'Actually I'm not a big football fan,' replies Rob looking down at the table as if there's some shame attached to not enjoying the game.

'So you'll be a rugby man then will you? I reckon Scotland hav bin doin' really well this season.'

'Er, no. To be honest I'm not much into sport.'

Fortunately the somewhat fruitless conversation is interrupted by the sound of the back door being opened.

'Aw that'll be owa Maureen with Kevin now. Brace yersels!'

The warning comes a bit late as an extremely muddy old English sheepdog with paws like dinner-plates, his tail wagging furiously, lopes into the kitchen and bounces off the walls, clearly beside himself with excitement to have visitors. Having chosen Rob as the first human for investigation he leaps at him, planting his muddy front paws on Rob's knee, his tongue lolling from a somewhat wet and dirty beard. Jackie immediately bellows at him,

'Kevin! No! Get doon! Ee, I'm so sorry Rob, he gets so excited. Here!' he says, rising from his chair and lungeing at Kevin's collar then dragging him into the utility room. 'Go on, dee as yer telt!' he shouts, quickly shutting the door before Kevin has the chance to escape. 'Ee, I'm so sorry Rob, 'e's made a right mess of yer trousers.'

'Oh don't worry,' replies Rob, staring down aghast at his favourite chinos. 'He's a friendly fellow isn't he?'

At that moment a somewhat dishevelled figure, liberally splattered with mud, squelches into the kitchen, her hair hanging in wet rats' tails.

'Ee hello. It's nice to meet you at last. Apologies for me rather bedraggled appearance but it's chuckin' it doon oot there. Mind owa Kevin's in fine fettle. 'Es been plodjin in the burn with the bairns from next door. They're dead canny but he's hacky dorty. 'E'd best stay in the scullery 'til he dries off, Jackie. Anyhow, how've you been you two? Did you have a good journey?'

'Yes, fine thanks,' I reply. 'We got the Metro from the airport to the Central Station and then through to Whitley Bay so it was fairly straight forward.'

'So what line of work are you in Jackie?' asks Rob.

'Me? Am in the poliss.'

'Sorry?' asks Rob, clearly confused.

'Am a copper. I used to wark in crime squad but am warkin in traffic now, ye na, nee nah, nee nah.'

'Oh right, that must be interesting. I guess you're kept pretty busy then?'

'Why aye, there's plenty of trouble round heor. We cover the whole of North Tyneside so there's neva a dull moment. We've got some intrestin' customers al say that much!'

'And what about you Maureen? Are you working?' I ask as Maureen drips her way over to the radiator to dry off.

'Aye pet, am teachin' English. A do Skype sessions, mainly for conversation like ye na.'

'Oh, that must be very rewarding,' replies Rob, quietly nudging my leg under the table. 'So where do your students come from?'

'Why, aal owa the place but China mainly. Speakin' of which a hope you'll excuse me but I've got a session in about twenty minutes so I'd better go get ready.'

'Of course, no problem,' I reply as a still-dripping Maureen heads for the stairs.

'We thought we'd eat at about half past five if that's okay with you two? We usually have tea a bit early cos we both tend to free-wheel through the day. And are you both happy with a curry? We just thought it'd be easier to have a take-away the night seeing as we've still got a bit of packing to do.'

'Of course, no problem,' smiles Rob.

'Maybe we could go and unpack our things, Jackie?' I suggest, 'and see you both later for dinner, er I mean tea,' I say, quickly correcting myself.

Our room is, unusually, on the ground floor and directly next to the downstairs bathroom.

'Well I guess you're going to have to get changed,' I remark, examining the muddy smears on Rob's trousers. Those are going to have to go straight in the wash when they've gone. Or maybe you should just wear them for dog-walking? It looks as though Kevin's going to be a bit of a handful.'

'You're telling me. He's a bit excitable to say the least. And tell me, how is it that you understand what they're saying? It's like a foreign language.'

'I was at University with a girl from Newcastle who had a really strong accent. I guess after three years I just picked up a lot of her expressions, but I agree, it is a bit tricky to understand, especially when they talk quickly.'

'You're telling me! I'm just glad you were able to translate.'

It's an hour later when we return to the kitchen, Rob clasping a bottle of Chianti that we'd managed to pick up at the airport.

'I don't know if it'll go with the curry but we thought you might enjoy this,' he says, offering the bottle to Maureen.

'Oh thank you, that's really kind of you,' smiles Maureen, looking at the label. 'Oh, is this that Chinese wine?'

Rob looks in my direction with a puzzled look.

'It's actually Italian,' he replies, 'from the Chianti region.'

'Oh, that's nice. I'll stick it in the fridge for later. We thought we'd start celebrating the start of our holiday early. Our Jackie's just gone to collect the Indian and then we can all have a glass when he gets back. I'm just going to go and feed Kevin but I'll keep him in the scullery. We don't want to ruin another pair of your trousers Rob!'

We're woken early the following morning by Kevin who, having witnessed Jackie and Maureen leave for the airport, is in need of comfort and attention. In spite of the fact that we assume he was left in the utility room he has somehow managed to escape and comes tearing into our room and hurls himself on the bed. There's a loud groan as he lands on Rob and starts wriggling around on his back with all four paws in the air.

'Good grief, he could have broken my ribs!' pants Rob, recovering from the attack. 'He weighs a ton Chris. That could have been a nasty accident.'

'Well tell him to get down. He shouldn't be in here anyhow, never mind on the bed. We ought to get up and get him out or he'll get over-excited and we'll have a puddle to clean up,' I say, sliding out of bed and grabbing my dressing-gown. However, Kevin clearly thinks that I've got out especially to play with him and, seeing me tying the belt of my dressing-gown, leaps off the bed, grabs hold of the end and starts pulling at it.

'No Kevin! Leave!' I say firmly but he really is excited and starts tearing around the bedroom and down the hallway, skidding on the rugs and sliding on the laminate floor. Within seconds he's back in the bedroom mounting another attack on Rob, this time with a squeaky toy in his mouth.

'There's no peace for the wicked!' I call, heading for the bathroom as a range of groans comes from under the bed-covers.

We spend the day familiarising ourselves with the area, a mainly residential part of the town but with long stretches of grass along the sea-front. Kevin is keen to be off the lead but we're far too nervous to consider letting him run free.

'Gosh he's hard work Chris,' wheezes Rob as Kevin heads off towards a lady walking a Yorkshire terrier, pulling Rob after him. Kevin rears up and emits a deep, throaty bark as the lady gives Rob a disapproving look, scoops her dog up into her arms and heads off determinedly in the opposite direction. 'I feel so guilty when he misbehaves but he's still curious bless him. He doesn't seem to have been socialised at all.'

'It could be that they've both been so busy working that they haven't had the time and you have to remember that in spite of his size he's still a puppy.'

'Well I hate to think what he's going to be like when he's fully grown if he doesn't learn to respond to a few basic commands. Anyhow, let's head home for a cup of tea. I could do with warming up.'

The following morning I wake with a splitting headache. A headache's unusual for me but this one's a blinder so Rob kindly agrees to walk Kevin while I try to prise my head from the pillow and make breakfast ready for their return. A shower helps to clear the brain-fog and by the time the pair of them get back everything is ready on the table. The back door opens and

Kevin comes bounding in, his paws matted with wet sand.

'Well that was a great walk wasn't it Kev?' exclaims Rob, staggering into the kitchen looking more than a little bedraggled and wind-blown. 'We had a really good stretch along the seafront and went down onto the sand. He had a whale of a time, didn't you boy?'

'Well that's good. Was it cold on the beach?' I ask.

'You know it's the North Sea that's for sure, but it was bracing. We met a really nice guy with a whippet called Wally.'

'Is that the dog or his owner?'

'The dog of course. He's a beauty. He and Kev had a great time playing. We got tied up in a bit of a knot but Kev was actually quite good with him. The owner's a nice fellow too. Must admit I didn't catch his name but he's kindly invited me out to the pub tomorrow night for a pint if that's okay with you darling?'

'No worries sweetheart. I'm impressed that you interpreted the invitation. So what sort of time are you going out?'

'I think he said he'd call round about eight so that gives us plenty of time for dinner.'

'You mean tea,' I correct.

'Speaking of tea, what are we having this evening?'

'Well I thought I'd have a night off and that maybe we could go out to eat, then I can do a big shop tomorrow.'

'That sounds like a good idea. Do you think Kevin'll be okay on his own?'

'I think so. I did ask and Jackie said he'd be fine for a couple of hours if we put him in the utility room, leave him with his chew and shut the door. I mean we wouldn't be out very long. Maureen said there's a nice little place down on the front that does really good fish and chips.'

'Excellent,' replies Rob, 'it's a date.'

The restaurant, if you could call it that, is somewhat jaded to say the least. The simple pine tables are furnished with plastic bucket-chairs in a rather startling, bright orange that reminds me of the old school canteen. The walls display a series of black and white photographs of fishermen and shipwrecks, some of which are partly obscured by the leaves of the rather dusty plastic plants that hang down from an overhead ledge.

We're led to a table by the window overlooking the sea-front by a waitress sporting a bright orange, sequinned t-shirt and black leggings. She's a big girl, probably in her early twenties, her short, spiky hair fetchingly dyed the same colour as her t-shirt.

'Can I be gettin' yous a drink while you're choosing?' she enquires, handing us each a menu that has clearly been around for some time, the pages stained by grease-marks.

'Er, yes please, that would be good,' replies Rob, smiling up at her. 'What wines have you got?'

'Well we've got red and we've got white,' she replies with an expressionless face, her pen hovering over her note-pad.

'Yes, but where do the wines come from?' asks Rob, the tone of his voice beginning to hint at his frustration.

'Why, I think they're from the Co-op. If you hang on I'll just go and ask the manager for you.'

'No, really, it's alright,' calls Rob after her as she heads off in the direction of the kitchen, at which point she stops and returns to our table.

'Oh, so have you made your minds up then?' she asks.

'We'll have a bottle of white please,' he replies.

'Good choice,' she replies. 'And are yous ready to order your food?' she asks, her face still totally expressionless.

'I think we'd both like fish and chips,' replies Rob, looking quizzically in my direction.

'Er, yes please. Do you have any haddock?' I ask, smiling at her in the hope she might thaw a little.

'No, I'm sorry we've only got fish,' she replies, at which point Rob puts his head in his hands.

'In which case we'll both have the fish and chips, thank you,' he says, handing back the menus.

'No problem,' she mutters. 'So will yous be wanting ordinary peas or mushy peas with that?'

'Oh mushy I think, don't you Chris?' asks Rob.

'Yes, and for me please,' I reply.

'Perfect,' she replies, and with that, waddles back to the kitchen with our order.

'Good grief, that was hard work!' laughs Rob. 'Let's hope the Co-op come up with a palatable bottle of wine! It feels more like being on an EasyJet flight in here than being in a restaurant. Let's just hope the food is edible.'

It's just over an hour later that we return to the house following our culinary experience which, in spite of the service and the decor, was surprisingly good. Kevin starts scratching at the utility room door, desperate to escape and wanting to play. Almost knocking us off our feet, he dashes into the sitting-room and comes back with a squeaky toy which he deposits at Rob's feet.

'It seems you're the chosen one,' I laugh as Rob picks up the toy and throws it across the room. Kevin's back with it in his mouth within seconds, drops it on the carpet and looks eagerly up at Rob through his shaggy fringe.

'I'm surprised he can see anything with all that hair Chris. It must take ages to groom him.'

'No doubt we'll find that out over the next couple of days,' I laugh. There's suddenly a strange noise from Kevin. And another. And another. 'Would you believe I think he's got hiccups?'

'I didn't know dogs could get hiccups,' muses Rob. 'Shall I try and give him a fright?'

'I don't think that would be a good idea. He hardly knows us and you might upset him.'

'Well we can't get him to drink out of the wrong side of his bowl or put cold keys down his back. What else can we do?' asks Rob as Kevin starts to look confused, not quite understanding what's happening to him as he continues to hiccup, his ribcage shuddering every few seconds.

'Oh poor fellow, he doesn't understand. Maybe I could try acupressure? It used to work on my cat.'

'Acupressure? What do you mean?'

'Well,' I say, walking over to try to calm Kevin, 'you find the bottom of the shoulder-blades, bring your hands in to the spine and then apply pressure on either side.' As I press down gently Kevin turns to look at me as if to ask me what I think I'm doing but, miraculously, the hiccups stop.

'Oh well done Dr Dolittle! That's amazing! Wherever did you learn to do that?'

'Well it works on humans so I just thought I'd apply the same technique and it seems to have done the trick.'

Rob ruffles Kevin's ears and then playfully pushes him to the floor where he rolls over to have his tummy tickled. 'Gosh he's huge Chris and he's still only a puppy. Goodness knows what he's going to be like by the time he's fully-grown.'

'Trouble with a capital T if they don't put some effort into training him a.s.a.p. He's already out of hand. Anyhow, let's take him round the block for his last walk and get to bed. I don't know about you but I'm whacked.'

We spend the following day exploring with Kevin who, with a bit of firm handling, walks quite well on the lead. He likes to greet everyone a little too exuberantly so we have to be firm with him to stop him jumping up on people, especially children. The youngsters love to say hello but he needs to be kept in check, especially if they have food in their hands. The air proves pretty bracing coming straight in off the North Sea, but it's also refreshing and good to be outside. The people seem really friendly, especially in the shops, and passers-by always greet us with a cheery 'hello'. I call into the local butcher's while Rob waits outside with Kevin.

'Hallo pet, and what can I be gettin' for you?' asks the rosy-faced man behind the counter.

'I'm just having a look thanks, we're on holiday here, well not quite a holiday, we're looking after someone's dog,' I reply.

'That must be Kevin is it?' he asks, stretching to look out of the door where Rob is having to restrain our furry friend from lurching into the shop.

'That's right. You obviously know him then?'

'Why aye, he's Jackie Rutherford's dog. Bit of a handful I believe,' he laughs.

'You could say that. Anyhow, I'll take a couple of pork chops and a couple of slices of that nice ham please.'

'Will you be wantin' some pease puddin' to go with it?' he asks as he puts a large ham on the slicer and starts carving off some thick slices.

'I'm not sure I know what pease pudding is,' I confess.

'It's a northern dish pet, made out of split peas but it's me nana's secret recipe. You'll love it, but you'll need to get some stotties to go with it.'

'Stotties?' I ask.

'Yes pet, stotty-cakes. They're bread-buns, you can get some round the corner at Gregg's.'

'Oh, right, thank you. That'll be all thanks,' I say reaching into my handbag for my purse.

'There you are then pet, and I've put a little something in the bag for Kevin. Have a nice day and hopefully we'll see you again.'

'Yes, thank you, I'm sure you will.'

As I step out of the shop Kevin immediately tries to stick his head in the bag. Clearly whatever is in there is tempting. 'Well that was kind, the butcher put something in the bag for

Kevin. They're such lovely people up here, there's always a warm welcome and a smile.'

We call at the baker's for some stotty-cakes and head back to the house. It's only when I unpack the bag that I realise why Kevin is so excited.

'Good grief, come and have a look at this!' I call, pulling out an enormous bone. 'It must be half a cow, it's absolutely enormous.'

'Crikey! That's more like a dinosaur bone, someone's going to be very happy.'

Kevin is already bouncing off the walls with excitement and leaping up to try and grab hold of his treat. Rob quickly takes hold of it, lifting it well out of Kevin's reach then orders him to sit in a very stern voice. To our surprise Kevin obeys and Rob offers the bone to him. He trots off to the utility room with it in his mouth and we can soon hear loud gnawing and slurping noises coming from one very happy puppy.

Our lunch of stotty-cakes filled with ham and pease pudding goes down well and we spend the afternoon quietly, even Kevin falling asleep having gorged on his trophy, his occasional whines and gentle, snuffly woofs hinting at doggy dreams.

It's shortly after dinner that evening that the doorbell rings.

'That must be my friend,' says Rob grabbing his jacket and his hat. 'I'll see you later darling. I won't be late.'

'Alright, have a good evening and don't drink too much!' I call, somewhat doubting that Rob will heed my words.

In spite of his resolve it's quite late in the evening by the time Rob returns from The Dog and Rabbit, clearly the merrier for his evening out.

'Well?' I ask.

'Well what?' he asks, falling into bed and dragging the covers off me.

'How did it go? Did you have a good evening?'

'I think so,' replies the muffled voice from under the duvet.

'What do you mean, "you think so"?'

'Well I think so because I didn't really understand much of what they were talking about,' replies the voice. 'But it was a really nice evening. Really nice.'

And before I know it snores are resounding through the depths of the mattress as my man falls instantly asleep.

It's during breakfast the following morning that the doorbell rings and Kevin immediately starts barking the house down.

'I wonder who that is?' I shout above the noise. 'It might be the postman. Can you keep hold of Kevin while I answer the door, love?'

Standing in the porch is a tall, well-built man with a big, bushy beard, probably in his fifties, clad in a yellow sou'wester, dungarees and heavy boots. He smiles warmly, removes his woolly hat and holds out a huge, rough hand in greeting.

'Oh good morning pet. You must be Rob's lovely missus. I'm Jem. I live just owa the way,' he says, pointing to a nearby row of terraced cottages. 'I was wondering if your Rob was ready like?'

'Ready?' I ask, somewhat confused. 'Er, might I ask what for?'

'Why aye. 'E kindly volunteered to be rescued last night in the pub, so I said I'd call by and give 'im a lift like.'

'Rescued? What do you mean, rescued?' I ask, somewhat confused, my imagination already running riot.

'It's the local life-boat crew, pet. We have to do a mock-up of rescuing someone and your hubby kindly said he'd be willing to volunteer,' he replies, rubbing his hands together and stepping from foot to foot.

'Could you just hold on a minute Jem? I'll just go and get him for you.' And with that I return swiftly to the kitchen where Rob is holding on to a very eager Kevin who's intent on leaping through the glass door that separates the kitchen from the hallway.

'Who is it darling?' asks Rob.

'It's a bloke called Jem who's come to collect you.'

'Collect me? What on earth for?'

'It seems that you volunteered to be rescued by the local life-boat crew,' I reply, folding my arms firmly across my chest and looking quizzically down at Rob.

'I did? But when? I don't remember volunteering for anything Chris. Are you sure he's got the right house?'

'Well he asked for you by name and referred to a conversation you had with him last night in the pub.'

'But seriously Chris, I don't remember anything about it and I only had two pints of Newcastle Brown so you can't accuse me of being drunk.'

'So how did the conversation go?' I ask. ' "Excuse me, but we're looking for a volunteer to be dropped into the North Sea and float around until our lot come and collect them?"'

'Well to be honest I didn't really understand much of what was being said, they were all talking so fast and they've all got such strong accents. Maybe I just nodded in the wrong place. I was trying to make out that I understood what they were saying because I felt such an idiot saying pardon all the time. Oh God Chris, what am I going to do? You know I'm not a strong swimmer and I'm terrified of being out of my depth and that's the North Sea for heaven's sake. It'll be bloody freezing!'

'Well maybe you should go and explain to Jem? It's a bit rude to keep him dancing around on the front doorstep.'

'Couldn't you tell him I'm not well?'

'Nope. I don't do lies, you know that Rob, especially when they're for other people. Go on, you're keeping him waiting.'

As Rob gets up from his chair I can already see the colour draining from his face. I try to listen in to the conversation through the glass door but the voices are too muffled and it's impossible to hear over Kevin's manic barking. It's a good few minutes later when Rob returns looking decidedly ashen.

'I don't know how to get out of this Chris. It seems they're already to go, they're all waiting for me down at the slipway. Jem assures me I'll only be in the water for a few minutes as their GPS tracking system will pick me up immediately and anyhow, they'll make a note of the drop-off point. They've got a wet-suit and a buoyancy aid for me so I'm not going to drown.'

'I should damn well hope not! Honestly Rob, I despair. You always manage to attract trouble. I'm coming with you.' And with that I head for the cloakroom and my coat.

'No Chris, please don't!' shouts Rob in a loud whisper. 'They're a macho bunch of blokes. I don't want them to think I need to bring my wife with me for heaven's sake. I'll be fine, really I will. I'll be back before you know it. You take Kevin out for his walk and I'll see you later.'

I don't like to add to Rob's anxiety but I'm seriously worried about the whole operation. His efforts at swimming have been a long-standing joke as he's never really progressed beyond a frantic doggy-paddle. Childhood memories of being taught to swim in a frog-infested pool full of green slime have left him mentally scarred so that actually getting him into the water is a real issue, the sea having to have warmed up to at least 17 degrees at the end of the summer, the tide creeping in gently over sun-baked sand. The serious cold of the water is already worrying me, not to mention his limited swimming ability.

'Right darling, I'm off. I'll see you soon and don't worry, I'll be fine,' he says, giving my cheek a farewell peck. However, the vibrato in his voice suggests he's feeling anything but. And with that he closes the kitchen door behind him.

I grab Kevin and bury my head in his fur, fighting back the tears but Kevin responds with a big sloppy kiss. Maybe a good walk will take my mind off it all.

The stress of the situation seems to have brought on another headache but the bracing sea air does help. We walk along the seafront towards the white dome of the Spanish City, an amusement park I've heard about but never seen. The building seems somewhat incongruous in a seaside setting. Kevin's intent on jumping up and chewing his lead, trying to pull it out of my hand and is bouncing around as though he's just downed a can of Red Bull. He manages to tie me round lamp-posts and drag me off in any direction except the one that I'm attempting to go in. There's loud music emanating from within the dome, so loud that my head throbs. I decide to head for the long stretch of grass along the links. The sea looks grey and cold and I can't help but worry about Rob, hardly bearing to think about how he's getting on, but reassure myself that he's in safe hands.

I find a bench to sit on while Kevin flops down with a loud sigh, staring up at me with doleful eyes before starting to chew the leg of the bench. I lean down to stroke his head and glance out to sea towards the lighthouse further up the coast. It looks bleak out there and white horses are beginning to form further out. As I turn my gaze I notice a ship exiting the mouth of the Tyne. It's a big brute and dwarfs the smaller craft that are already out on the water.

'Come on Kevin, let's head home and see if Uncle Rob's back yet. He should have finished his ordeal by now,' I say, slipping a treat from my pocket into an eager mouth. He wags his tail furiously and, as we start walking again, begins to leap up and grab his lead. I'm feeling wrecked and head for home and a cup of tea.

Over an hour later there's still no sign of Rob. His mobile is lying on the kitchen table so there's no chance of calling him. It occurs to me that the crew might have taken him for a pint as a thank you so tell myself not to worry. Kevin has dribbled all over the glass coffee table in the lounge and is now chewing on what is left of his bone. Two cups of tea and another dose of paracetamol and at last there's a noise in the hall. Kevin leaps up to investigate and begins another bout of frantic barking. I open the door just in time to see an ambulance pull away, the driver giving a friendly wave, to find Rob clinging onto the doorframe, his body shaking uncontrollably.

'Darling, what on earth's happened? Come on, let's get you sat down. Oh my God, you poor thing.' Rob takes hold of my arm as I guide him carefully to the settee and ease him down gently. 'Let me get you a blanket and then you can tell me all about it.' I say, rushing into the bedroom to grab the duvet. 'So what happened sweetheart?' I ask, wrapping the duvet around his shoulders and tucking it around his body. 'Couldn't they find you? How long were you in the water?'

'I wwwasn't in the wwwater very long. That wasn't the pproblem,' he replies, his lower lip wobbling and his teeth chattering.

I'm finding it hard to fathom out what's happened. 'Okay, so tell me from the beginning.'

'Well they dressed me up and took me out to the drop-off ppoint.'

'Yes, and then what?'

'They said that the tteam would be wwith me in no time so I just bbobbed around wwaiting for them.'

'Go on.'

'I was wwondering where they'd got to when ssuddenly I heard this terrible whooshing noise. To be honest I thought I was ddying.'

'Oh my poor love, so what was it?'

'Well I managed to tturn myself round and saw this huge ship hheading towards me and someone was shouting ddown to me.'

'Oh my God Rob, you could have been killed.'

'Well that was my ffear but this guy was shouting, "Don't worry, we're coming to rescue you". Of ccourse I ddidn't want rescuing, so I was shouting back telling him I didn't want rescuing because I was wwaiting to be rescued.'

'If this wasn't so awful it would be funny. So did you persuade them to leave you in the water?'

'Nno. They insisted because there's ssome law that says you have to try and rescue a mman overboard.'

'Oh Lord, so what happened next?'

'They lowered one of their ttenders and two bblokes hauled me out of the water, wrapped me in a ffoil blanket and shot off back to North Shields with me. It was the DFDS Newcastle to Amsterdam ferry that ppicked me up.'

'So what happened to the lifeboat crew who were searching for you? They must have been frantic.'

'The fferry company radioed them to explain what had happened and a mmember of the team drove round to collect me. I was in ssuch a bad way, more from shock than ccold, that they ccalled an ambulance.'

'Good grief, what an awful experience darling. Let me go and make you a hot drink and then let's get you to bed.'

'There isn't anything stronger is there Chris? I could mmurder a bbrandy.'

It's a good four hours before a still sleepy head appears round the door. Kevin leaps up from where he's been lying and presents Rob with his tuggy rope.

'I don't know that Uncle Rob's got the strength to play Kevin.'

'Uncle Rob's doing fine now thank you Aunty Christine. Here Kev,' he says, grabbing one end of the rope and pulling Kevin across the floor. 'Oh and by the way darling, the Lifeboat crew have invited me to join them on Saturday.'

'Oh Rob, is this wise? I hope you're not going drinking again.'

'No, they've invited me to go and watch Newcastle play Liverpool. Apparently the tickets are like gold dust. I know it's not normally my sort of thing but it would have been rude to say no, it's a very generous thank you.'

'I suppose you're right but please keep off the beer Rob. It's pretty lethal stuff. It's a lot stronger than people realise.'

'I'll be absolutely fine pet, divn't you worry,' replies my man in a mock-Geordie accent, laughing and grabbing hold of Kevin's lead. 'I'm going to take this boy for a walk to give you a rest. I think it's been as much of an ordeal for you as it has for me.'

'Alright but be careful, and no more adventures, we've had enough for one house-sit.'

'We'll be fine won't we Kev?' Rob says opening the back door and, as he disappears down the path I'm sure I hear him calling, 'Haway the lads!'

STRANGER IN PARADISE

'OH ROB, YOU'LL NEVER guess who's on tour in the UK?' I shout excitedly.

'No idea,' comes the voice from the kitchen. 'Barry Manilow?'

'No, and stop teasing me. Try again.'

'Neil Diamond?'

'Hardly, he's in his 80s.'

'Really? I didn't realise he was that old, but then so is Tom Jones and it hasn't stopped him. Anyhow, put me out of my misery, who is it?' he asks coming through to the sitting-room.

'Rod Stewart!'

'Oh wow! Now you're talking. When's he going to be around?'

'Not until October but the tickets go on sale this Friday.'

'So where's he going to be performing?'

'Mmmm, let me have a look. Sheffield, Newcastle, Manchester, Birmingham, Leeds and London.'

'Well I'm sure we could manage one of those providing we can get tickets.'

'The trouble is they'll sell really quickly and the fan club always get first pick, but I'll have a look. Where do you think would be best? I can't face London but we could fly direct to Manchester or Birmingham and the accommodation would be cheaper.'

'That's true, but by the time we've bought tickets and paid for flights and a hotel room it's all going to get pretty expensive Chris. You're talking at least £500 and that's before we start eating out.'

'I guess you're right, maybe we should just forget the idea. Unless of course …'

'Unless of course what?'

'We can find a house-sit.'

'Now there's an idea! But the problem would be finding something that coincided with the concert and was in the area. It would also need to be an animal that could be left for a few hours. That sounds a bit complicated.'

'Well I can have a go, it's worth a try. The transport system in Birmingham is good and the concert hall is bang in the middle. I'll have a look and see if there's anything that fits the bill.'

The 'Paradise B&B' fits the bill perfectly. An impressive red-brick Victorian house situated in the leafy suburb of Edgbaston. It's close to the station, the shops and the canal so ticks most of the boxes. A brief exchange of messages informs me that the owners, an elderly couple called Fred and Betty, have apparently been having difficulty finding sitters so they're delighted that we're interested in helping them out.

'So what's the animal Chris? I take it it's a dog?'

'It is but I can't pretend that I'm too enthused.'

'Why? That's not like you.'

'I know, but it's a Chihuahua.'

'What's the problem with Chihuahuas?'

'I don't know. I think it's because they're so small and this one's absolutely tiny. I'm a big dog person. Tiny ones make me nervous, especially if they've got short hair.'

'Is it one of those tea-cup things?'

'I don't really know. They don't say so in the details but it is horribly small. Good grief, and it's called Cha-Cha! She's 14 years old apparently.'

'Cha-Cha? That's a peculiar name but 14's a good age.'

'Yes, but I think it's one of the breeds that lives much longer, like Yorkshire Terriers. I read somewhere that someone had one that went on into its twenties.'

'Crikey! Any idea why they've been having difficulty getting sitters?' queries Rob coming to look over my shoulder at the photos.

'No, but I'll have a look at the reviews, that might give us a clue,' I reply, scrawling to the review section on the web-site. 'They've only ever had three lots of sitters which doesn't help much and they've all been pretty brief with their feed-back.'

'Well maybe like you they weren't keen on Chihuahuas but didn't want to upset the owners.'

'It could be, I mean they can be very yappy and I'm sure that I read somewhere that they're high up the list of dogs that bite.'

'But surely they couldn't do you much damage? It's not as though there's any weight behind them.'

'I wouldn't be so sure about that.'

'So what are we saying? Do you want to give it a go or not?'

'Well there's nothing else in Birmingham with dates that would cover us going to the concert so I guess it has to be a yes, but I'll wait until we know for definite that we've got tickets before we accept.'

It's several weeks later when we find ourselves at the revamped Birmingham New Street Station whose architect clearly seemed to think that making it look as though the whole building has been wrapped in a huge sheet of tinfoil was a good idea. The whole place seems horribly crowded, something we're just not used to at home, so it all feels a bit daunting.

'According to Betty we need to get the number 80 bus and get off at Church Road, then it's only a five minute walk,' I inform Rob, looking at my notes.

'Lead on boss,' replies Rob, wheeling his suitcase behind him.

A bus-ride later and we're standing outside a red brick house which is handsomely decorated with Victorian tiles, the upper storey clad with a mock timber-frame. A sign that overhangs the outer wall reads, 'Paradise B&B' and below it, suspended on a chain, 'No Vacancies'.

'Well that's a relief!' laughs Rob looking at the sign. 'I reckon this dog's going to be enough to keep us busy.'

On entering the garden we can't help but notice a rather large caravan parked under some trees, so maybe our hosts are off for a few days. We ring the door bell and can immediately hear high-pitched yapping coming from inside. We're soon greeted by a rather stooped and slightly wizened gentleman who peers round the side of the door. He's clearly wearing a rather badly-fitting toupée in a colour that is far too dark for his years.

'Hallo! You must be the sitters. Come on in then,' he says smiling, his voice reflecting a rich Brummie accent. 'The wife's just sorting some stuff out upstairs. Here, put your cases down there and let me take your coats.'

'Thank you, that's very kind,' says Rob slipping his coat off. 'You must be Fred, pleased to meet you,' he says holding out his hand.

'And nice to meet you too,' replies Fred, lifting his voice above the yapping and smiling up at Rob. 'If you'd like to take a seat in the lounge Betty should be down soon. I'll just go and hang your coats up.'

'Thank you,' replies Rob as we head through the door into the sitting-room.

It's a spacious room with high ceilings but rather dark as it's overshadowed by some large trees directly outside the window. The decor is rather old-fashioned but everything is very neat and immaculately clean. Two alcoves on either side of a large Victorian tiled fireplace are lined with red, flock wallpaper, the sort that's often seen in Indian restaurants that my mother used to covet. A number of framed photographs are lined up on the mantlepiece and I wander over to have a look while we wait for Fred to return. They're clearly photos of Fred and Betty, all of them showing them ballroom dancing through the years. They really look quite something in their early days, Betty with an incredible figure and Fred looking very handsome in his tail-coat. I'm just about to comment on them when Fred returns.

'I was just admiring your photos here Fred, you must have done well by the looks of things?'

'Oh yes Babs, we were the leading dancers in all the competitions for years. We won the trophy at the Tower Ballroom and the Locarno six years running when we were in our thirties.'

'So are you still dancing?'

'Oh yes. We'll never stop dancing as long as our legs can hold us up.'

'Are you off in the caravan then Fred?' asks Rob, settling down on the sofa.

'No, no lad, we're off on a cruise,' replies Fred, turning to Rob. 'Betty and I work on board ship once a year. We run classes and organise the tea dances. We leave Southampton on Saturday which is why we needed someone to look after Cha-Cha.'

'Ah, so now I know how she got her name!' I smile.

At that moment I can hear footsteps in the hall and a very glamorous Betty sashays in to greet us. She's every inch the dancer, her head held high, shoulders back and with a gentle sway to her movement. Considering she must be in her eighties she's in excellent shape. She's beautifully made up and smartly dressed in a figure-hugging dress in a fetching shade of powder blue and a pair of high heels. The only thing that seems incongruous is her white hair which is tightly permed in a style that might have been popular in the seventies but now looks decidedly dated. She walks gracefully over to shake hands.

'Hello, you must be Christine,' she smiles. 'And this must be Robert, how do you do?'

I'm immediately struck by the posh Brummie accent which sounds rather peculiar.

'I hope that Fred has made you comfortable? Fred,' she says turning to her husband, 'have you offered our visitors a cup of tea, or maybe they would like a glass of Proseccio? What do you say you two? After all, we are all on holiday now aren't we?'

'A glass of Prosecco would be lovely, thank you Betty,' replies Rob.

'And just a small one for me Frederick because I'm driving,' she calls through to the hallway.

As Fred disappears through to the kitchen the constant yapping intensifies.

'Oh that's Cha-Cha. She'll do this until she's met you. I'd better go and get her or it'll go on all afternoon,' says Betty apologetically.

She returns with Cha-Cha tucked firmly under her arm. She's a pretty little thing with long, chestnut and white fur and a tiny, round head like an apple. We immediately notice, however, that our new charge is wearing a dress and look at one another askance. Rob gets up and walks over to greet her but is immediately met by a threatening growl as Cha-Cha tries to lunge out of Betty's arms and hurl herself at him.

'Now now Cha-Cha, calm down!' commands Betty, wrestling with the squirming creature in her arms and looking flustered. 'She'll be like this until she knows you're not a threat. She's very protective of me and of her things but she will calm down eventually, don't worry.'

Rob has already backed off and I have no intention of getting any closer. Fred returns carrying a brass tray decorated with a doily on which four glasses of Prosecco and a bowl of peanuts are arranged.

'Eer yar' he says, placing the tray on a large, glass-topped coffee table. 'One for you Babs,' he says, handing me a glass, 'and one for the gentleman.'

'Well, here's to a happy stay you two,' says Betty managing to take a glass while still struggling to restrain Cha-Cha. 'I hope you have an enjoyable time while we're away. Oh, and I've left you some salad in the fridge for your tea. There's some ham and cheese and a bag of mixed leaves, oh and some coldslaw and a couple of advocados. I think they're orgasmic. Feel free to help yourselves to anything from the cupboards.'

'Thank you Betty, that's very kind,' I say trying not to laugh as Rob is choking on his Prosecco. 'So when will you be back exactly?'

'It'll be exactly two weeks providing there are no delays. I've written everything down for you in the notes. All the information about feeding Cha-Cha and her routine is all there and of course, the vet's contact.'

'That's really helpful Betty, thank you. And we'll be in touch to let you know how we're getting on.'

'That would be lovely but bear in mind we might not always have a signal.'

'So where is the cruise heading?' asks Rob.

'The Canaries,' replies Fred. 'We stop off at Lisbon before doing the islands and then Madeira on the way back. We travel for free of course, all meals included so it's worth our while and it means that we keep up with our dancing. Mind you, I'm beginning to feel my age now and my arthritis is so painful it slows me down. But it's good for us to get a break from the B&B.'

'Speaking of which,' interrupts Betty, 'we've put the no vacancies sign up and we haven't got any bookings so you needn't worry about that side of things. Anyhow, if you'll excuse us we'd better be making a move, we've got a long journey ahead of us. I'll pop Cha-Cha in the kitchen while we leave so she doesn't get upset.' And with that Betty glides through the door, still clasping Cha-Cha in her arms.

Betty and Fred having driven off we think we'd better go and make friends with Cha-Cha but approaching the kitchen door the yapping turns into a growl.

'I hope she doesn't go for us,' says Rob, placing his hand on the doorknob.

'Let's hope her bark is worse than her bite,' I reply, quietly worried that we might be in for some trouble.

'Hello Cha-Cha,' says Rob quietly opening the door. 'Let's say hello little one.'

Cha-Cha has other ideas and immediately launches herself at Rob's legs, grabbing hold of his trouser leg and shaking it as if to kill. Rob's immediate reaction is to lift his leg out of her grasp but she clings on with her teeth and is hoisted into the air.

'Good grief Chris, help me!' he shouts, trying to dislodge her from his trouser-leg.

'What do you expect me to do? I'm going to get bitten if I try to hold her.'

'Well find something to distract her for God's sake before she ruins my best cords.'

I look around the kitchen for something and manage to find a basket full of toys in the corner of the room. 'Here Cha-Cha!' I call waving a stuffed giraffe in her direction. Despite the fact that the giraffe is actually bigger than her she releases her grip on Rob's trouser-leg, runs over to me and wraps her teeth round the giraffe instead. It receives the same treatment as the trousers as she shakes it furiously in her mouth, growling continuously.

'I think I'm beginning to understand why they were having difficulty finding sitters,' remarks Rob, his voice quivering from the shock of the attack. 'She's going to take some taming, that's for sure. Maybe a treat will convince her we're friendly?'

'It also means we're rewarding bad behaviour,' I reply disapprovingly.

'They must have some in here somewhere,' says Rob, ignoring my comment. 'Let's have a look in the notes and see what they say.' And with that he heads for the kitchen dresser and picks up the folder of instructions. 'Yup, there's supposed to be a jar here somewhere. Ah, here we are,' he says removing a large ceramic jar from one of the shelves. The moment Cha-Cha hears the lid being removed she's by Rob's side sitting nicely and staring up at him. 'Oh, so you know that sound do you you savage creature?' he says, staring down at her. 'And you know what to do to get a treat too! Good girl!' he says soothingly, bending down and warily offering her the treat. Surprisingly she takes it nicely from his hand and trots off to her basket to enjoy it.

'Well, I suppose that's a bit of progress,' I remark, 'but what are we supposed to do about that thing that she's wearing? I don't fancy our chances trying to get it off her.'

'Well let's not worry about that for the moment. I think we need to make friends before we try undressing her, and the notes suggest we need to brush her daily. That should be fun! I suggest that you go and unpack our case and I'll stay here with her.'

'If you're sure, but scream if you need help,' I say and head off up the stairs.

I spend some time putting our clothes and toiletries away before heading back to the kitchen. On opening the door I'm amazed to find Rob lying on the kitchen floor with his back against the dresser, fast asleep and with Cha-Cha curled up on his lap snoring gently. She's clearly decided he's alright after all. I decide I'd better go in search of Cha-Cha's coats which, according to the notes are in the Turret Room.

It's a rambling old place but all in pristine condition. Clearly the need to keep it immaculate is a result of the B&B business but how Fred and Betty manage it at their age I really don't know, I can only assume that they have help. There are four guest bedrooms, all en suite, and a corridor leading into the part of the house that resembles a turret. I open the huge, wooden door tentatively, not knowing what to expect. To my amazement, there before me is a rail of clothing that wouldn't look out of place in a theatre. It's clearly Betty's collection of ballroom dresses, all enclosed in plastic covers. There are sequins and feathers, lamé and chiffon, fringes and tassels in an array of colours and arranged neatly below them are a collection of dancing shoes. It's a veritable treasure trove. It must have been wonderful to be waltzed around a ballroom wearing such beautiful dresses.

Just as I'm about to leave I notice a smaller rail on the other side of the room which is also hung with clothing. Dog's clothing. This is clearly Cha-Cha's wardrobe but could easily rival Betty's. There must be over fifty outfits from bumble bees to dinosaurs to fairies and dragons. There are net skirts and tiaras, rabbit's ears and antlers. The collection must be worth a fortune. I recall Betty saying that Cha-Cha needed to wear outfits to keep her warm as, being such a tiny dog, she is prone to getting cold quickly. However, in my naivety, I'd imagined they'd be standard coats not fancy-dress outfits. I'm not so sure that Rob'll be too thrilled when I tell him.

I return to the kitchen only to find him and Cha-Cha in exactly the position I'd left them in. I lean forward and take Rob gently by the shoulder but my actions wake Cha-Cha who immediately resumes her throaty growl and, curling back her lips, bares her teeth at me. Her growling wakes Rob who comes to with a start.

'Oh, sorry darling. Had I nodded off?'

'Yes, you and your new friend were off with the fairies. You must have been tired after our journey and I didn't like to wake you. She seems to have taken a shine to you but I'm clearly still on the not-so-sure list. I think we'd better feed her, have a bite to eat ourselves then let her out into the garden and head for bed. Hopefully tomorrow we can get into a bit of a routine.'

Later that night, having climbed into bed, we both find it difficult to settle, probably because the room is new to us and the bed a little lumpy. Neither of us seems to be able to get to sleep. I lie there thinking through the day's events.

'Did you ever have a perm?' I ask Rob.

'What on earth makes you ask that?' laughs Rob. 'No, I didn't, why?'

'I was just thinking about Betty's hairdo, it's still so 1970s, you know when everyone had perms like Petula Clark, including the men?'

'Yes I do remember. Lots of blokes had perms, especially the footballers. Let's think, there was Keegan and Souness.'

'That's right, and the Beatles. George and Ringo both had them.'

'So did you have one in your former life?'

'Yes of course. Did I never tell you the story about my perm and the school trip?'

'No, but I have a feeling you're going to tell me anyhow,' replies Rob, turning on his side and snuggling in to me. 'Go on.'

'Well, it was before we worked together obviously, when I was school secretary to the previous headmaster, old Robins.'

'You mean headteacher darling, you're not allowed to call them headmasters any more,' corrects Rob.

'Alright, headteacher. We'd organised the annual school trip for the top juniors to go to France for the day and I went along as usual as I made most of the arrangements and they needed an extra pair of hands.'

'Crikey, that must have been quite a trek, what with the ferry crossing and everything?'

'It was, but we always enjoyed it and the kids loved it. Anyhow, we were on the way back in the coach from France, just north of Dover, when one of the lads came up to me and said that his friend, Brian, was acting a bit odd. Obviously I went to investigate so I sat down in the seat next to him to try and find out what was wrong.'

'And?'

'Well he was acting very strangely. He was sitting in his seat kicking his legs out and poking the back of the seat in front of him.'

'Oh, that sounds a bit weird, so go on.'

'I asked him what he was doing and he said he was watching the World Cup! Clearly he thought the back of the seat was the TV screen and he thought he was pressing the buttons to change the channel. His feet were thrashing about as though he was trying to kick a ball. I had no idea what to do as his behaviour was so bizarre. Then his mate,' I start laughing at the thought of what happened, 'leant over the aisle and asked me what Brian was doing. When I explained that Brian thought he was watching the World Cup on the television his friend said, "Can you ask him what the score is?"'

'Oh crikey, that's priceless Chris, but what's this got to do with perms?'

'I'm getting to that bit, this is quite a long story. Brian was beginning to worry me and so I asked the kids if anyone had noticed him take anything, at which point one of the girls said she'd seen him get something out of his bag. So, I got his bag down off the rack and had a look inside in case there were any clues. Sure enough, there was a blister pack of travel sickness tablets and four of them were empty. I reckon he'd overdosed and was hallucinating.'

'But that could have been really serious, what on earth did you do?'

'Well I went and told Mr Robins and we agreed that we needed to get him to a hospital. The coach driver was very co-operative and we managed to make a detour to the nearest A and E. I managed to get him into the hospital where we were asked to go into a consulting room and I explained to the doctor what had happened Anyhow, he reckoned that Brian would be fine once the tablets wore off so we got back on the coach and off we went again. Old Robins offered to sit with him to give me a break as it was all getting a bit stressful.'

'I can imagine, but I'm still waiting to know what this has to do with you having a perm?'

'Nearly there. We'd been back on the road for about an hour when old Robins beckoned to me to come to where they were sitting and told me that he thought Brian was okay now. He turned to him and said, "So who am I Brian?" to which Brian replied, "Mr Robins". Old Robins turned to me and smiled and then, pointing at me, he asked, "And who's this Brian?" to which

Brian replied, "Kevin Keegan!"

We both start rolling around the bed with tears streaming down our faces.

'Oh that's a gem!' howls Rob. 'So how did it end? The poor lad must have felt really stupid the day after.'

'Well I was sensitive to that so I asked the rest of the class not to mention it to Brian. But apparently, the next day when his class teacher asked them all to draw a picture of their day out, the poor lad was just sitting staring at a blank piece of paper. His memory was totally wiped, he didn't even know he'd been to France!'

'Oh the poor chap. How humiliating, but you were lucky he came through it unscathed. Anyhow, let's try and get some sleep, it's really late but at least we can have a nice lazy day tomorrow.'

'Well I suppose so but we're going to have to leave about half past six,' I remind him.

'Leave? Why? Are we going somewhere?' asks Rob with surprise.

'You know jolly well we are, it's the Rod Stewart concert, remember? The reason we came to Birmingham in the first place?'

'Darling I'm so sorry and I jest not, I truly had forgotten. It must have been all the excitement.'

'You are hopeless Robert Baird. We'll need to get into town and then to the National Exhibition Centre and don't forget it'll be busy so we need to allow plenty of time.'

'So have you brought your leather trousers?'

'No I have not and I hope you haven't got anything hidden away in your extensive wardrobe like a pair of leopardskin ones,' I laugh, turning over and yanking the duvet over to my side. 'Anyhow, night night,' I whisper. But Rob is already fast asleep.

The next morning we enter the kitchen cautiously only to find Cha-Cha curled up in her basket, still soundo. She's shivering, her tiny body trembling, and occasionally one of her legs jerks in what seems to be a spasm. She's still wearing the dress that she had on when we arrived as we've been too nervous to remove it.

'Oh come and look Rob, she's so sweet when she's asleep,' I whisper. However, my whisper is enough to wake her and we're immediately greeted by a succession of high-pitched yaps.

'Oh not again. This is going to be a pain,' sighs Rob. 'Let's see if we can find her food and get something in her mouth to shut her up,' he suggests heading for the pantry. Cha-Cha is immediately by his side, her little tail wagging furiously but her yapping has turned to the most peculiar noise. It's more akin to a bird talking.

'I don't know what she's trying to tell you Rob, isn't it weird?'

'It is a bit peculiar that's for sure,' he laughs setting her bowl down on the floor. 'So are we going to go and explore this morning?' he asks, sitting down to breakfast.

'Yes, I thought we could find our way over to the canal and walk along the towpath. The notes say that a fifteen minute walk is enough for Cha-Cha but you could always carry her the rest of the way if she gets tired.'

'I could? You're the one with the handbag not me. I refuse to be seen carrying a Chihuahua.'

'Why not for heaven's sake?'

'It's not manly, that's why.'

'Oh Rob, don't be so ridiculous, a dog is a dog.'

'Yes, but not one that's wearing a dress.'

'That's a point, we'd better find something more becoming from her extensive wardrobe. I'll go and see what I can find after breakfast.'

After clearing the table I climb up to the Turret Room to select something from the rail. Trying to find something inconspicuous is quite a challenge but I return with a small houndstooth coat. 'Here we are. You'll be pleased to know that I left the matching hat behind.'

'Well at least it's better than this dress. If I hold onto her maybe you could try and get this thing off her?'

'Alright but just keep her teeth away from me. She may be small but those teeth look like needles.'

It's a huge struggle which involves much growling from Cha-Cha but between us we manage to disrobe her and then dress her in the coat. She does at least look slightly less ridiculous.

The towpath proves popular with walkers, joggers and dog-walkers but as the path is narrow in places we often have to give way to other users. Cha-Cha proves fearless when meeting other dogs and lets them know very quickly if they've overstayed their welcome. She attracts a lot of attention simply because she's so tiny and we're made to feel guilty for letting this poor little thing actually walk.

'You could do with one of those sling things Chris, you know the ones that you hang round your neck to carry the dog in,' remarks Rob.

'Oh could I? I could just stuff her up your jumper and you could carry her, she'll have had enough by now and we've still got to get her home.'

'No way. If anyone's carrying her it's you.'

'But she doesn't like me, she'll growl and I'm not going to risk her lunging at my face again.'

'Oh alright, I'll take her,' says Rob grumpily, leaning over and picking Cha-Cha up. 'I reckon she'd fit in my pocket, don't you?'

'Well you could try it I suppose,' I reply dubiously, 'but I'm not sure she's going to like it.'

But she does like it, in fact she seems very contented and sits with her head hanging over the top of Rob's pocket watching the world go by like a doggy kangaroo. A brightly-painted narrowboat cruises slowly past and the woman at the tiller gives us a friendly wave.

'Do you realise that Birmingham has more miles of canal

than Venice?' I ask Rob, linking his arm as we saunter along.

'Really? That's hard to believe.'

'Well you have to remember that the waterways were the main form of transport for many years before someone invented the steam train. Once the trains came along many of the canals proved too slow and fell into disuse.'

'You're a font of information this morning Mrs Baird,' Rob laughs, squeezing my arm. 'So which canal is this one?'

'The Worcester and Birmingham. You can actually get all the way to the River Severn from here.'

'Crikey, that would take forever. Quicker on the motorway,' he laughs.

'Yes, but not so pretty. Anyhow, I think it's about time we turned round and headed back to the house. We need time to get into our glad rags and I think we'd better have a snack before we leave.'

On arriving back in the street we notice a huge lorry parked outside the house. It's got a foreign registration that we don't recognise. It's only on getting closer that we realise it's Irish and the name Monaghan's is printed in huge letters along the side against a background of the Irish flag.

'That's odd Chris, I wonder why he's parked here? It's a bit strange to see a brute like that in a residential area.'

It's just as we turn into the driveway that we hear the cab door open and a rather substantial man dressed in overalls jumps down to the pavement and heads in our direction. Cha-Cha immediately starts barking excitedly and Rob has difficulty stopping her from leaping out of his pocket.

'Hallo there!' calls the man. 'It's no use ringing the bell, there doesn't seem to be anyone at home. I've been here for the last half hour.' It's at this point that he notices Cha-Cha and comes running up to Rob. 'Well hallo there me darlin',' he says, leaning forward and stroking her head. 'Have you been missin' yer

Uncle Seamus Cha-Cha? There's a good little girl now.'

Cha-Cha is clearly delighted to see him and, as he reaches forward to take hold of her she's already trying to climb out of Rob's pocket so that she can be picked up. She looks even tinier in the man's hands but is licking his face and whimpering with pleasure.

'So you two clearly know each other,' remarks Rob.

'Good gracious me yes, we go back a long time Cha-Cha and me, don't we sweetheart?' he says, cuddling her and rubbing her ears. 'Must be five years I've been coming here now. So are you two staying with Fred and Betty?'

'Now quite,' I reply, 'we're actually looking after the place while they're away.'

'Away? Oh. They never told me they were going away. And where is it they've gone?'

'On a short holiday,' I reply, not wanting to give the stranger too much information.

'But I'm assuming they told you that I was coming?' he asks looking slightly worried.

'Coming?' I ask, now feeling slightly worried myself.

'I have a booking for this evening. I always stay here before I head back to the ferry. I've been doing it for years, last week of the month on a Friday.'

This suddenly seems incredibly awkward. Do we turn him away or do we honour his booking and have to cater for a total stranger? I turn and look pleadingly at Rob who is clearly feeling as flustered as I am. We're both thinking on our feet.

'Er, well clearly this is a bit difficult Seamus, I'm assuming that's your name?' Rob explains.

'It is to be sure,' replies our visitor looking appealingly at Rob.

'I mean we didn't know you were coming and we don't know who you are. I hope you can see it from our point of view? It's a little bit difficult to entertain you in a house that doesn't actually belong to us if you see what I mean?'

'I do sir, but I assure you, I could describe the inside of that house as if it were me own. You go in the door and then …'.

'Yes, I'm sure you can Seamus, but it doesn't seem right for us to allow you to stay when we haven't had any instructions from Betty and Fred.'

'Well here, I can show you me paperwork,' he says, reaching into his pocket with one hand and trying not to drop Cha-Cha. 'Here, Paradise B&B, one night, paid with thanks, E and F Henderson.'

'Er, yes, I can see that that's all in order,' replies Rob looking increasingly flustered.

'So what am I supposed to do?' asks Seamus, his voice becoming suddenly assertive, 'I've already paid for me bed and breakfast. Maybe we could try and phone them? Have they gone far?'

'The Canaries,' I reply, beginning to feel increasingly ill at ease.

'Well look. How's about I try to phone them?' he suggests. 'I've got their number right here.'

'I'll tell you what Seamus, I'll ring them myself,' replies Rob. 'Excuse me if we just go into the house for a moment. We'll be right back.' And at that we remove Cha-Cha from under his arm and head into the house.

'Crikey, this is a horribly awkward situation Chris. I'll just have to hope we can get hold of Betty.'

'Yes, but what if she says it's okay? We're going to have to put up with him in the house for the night and we're supposed to be going to the concert.'

'Well I suppose that if we do have to we can cope,' replies Rob looking concerned.

'But what about the concert?' I cry. 'We can't go out and leave him alone in the house. What if we pretend we couldn't get hold of Betty and that we don't feel able to accommodate him?'

'Mmm, a bit difficult because he could phone her himself and he'd find out about it when he next came to stay. Oh this is messy. Give me a moment and I'll try to get hold of Betty.'

Surprisingly the phone is answered almost immediately but I can only hear one side of the conversation. Rob has explained the situation and is obviously awaiting Betty's response.

'Yes … no I know that … yes but … well I suppose so but you must appreciate it is a bit awkward I mean … no I appreciate that but … Alright, so he's to stay in the Samba Suite … and it's a full English, I'll let Chris know,' he says looking anxiously in my direction. 'Yes, alright Betty, I'm sure we'll manage. Thanks. Goodbye.'

On ending the call Rob looks apologetically at me. 'I'm sorry love, I couldn't really get us out of it. She says that he can look after himself but would we be good enough to do him a cooked breakfast.'

'But we haven't got the ingredients for a cooked breakfast so now I'm going to have to go shopping as well. And what are we going to do about Rod?' I say getting choked up by the disappointment.

'Well I've been giving it some thought. As you say we can hardly leave Seamus here on his own so I suggest that I stay and you go and see Rod.'

'What? On my own? I don't want to go on my own and anyhow I wouldn't want to risk going into Birmingham alone and then having to get back late at night. Oh Rob, this is so unfair, I was so looking forward to it! You do realise that this could be his last tour?' I wail.

'I'm sorry darling but I can't see a way out of it. Anyhow, I'd better go and tell Seamus that he's got a bed for the night.'

'And I suppose I'd better go shopping,' I sigh, stomping off to the kitchen for a shopping bag.

By the time I get back with the groceries Rob and Seamus are happily seated round the table, each with a glass in their hand.

'Yes, to be sure Rob, it's a clever cover-up. No-one would ever know now would they?' says Seamus taking a slug from his glass. 'I mean who would suspect that a huge lorry like mine was packed to the gills with Irish whiskey?'

My heart sinks as I realise that one of the bottles seems to have made its way onto the kitchen table.

'Of course the lorry's empty now as I'm heading back to Dublin but,' he lowers his voice and leans over towards Rob, 'I always keep a bottle or two in the cab in case of emergencies. Would you like another drop Rob, or is it a "wee dram" you'd be wantin'?'

'That would be most acceptable Seamus. Thank you,' replies Rob holding out his glass.

Seamus pours a rather generous amount into Rob's glass then cries '*Sláinte!*'

'*Sláinte!*' cries Rob in return, chinking glasses with his new friend.

'Well hello Christine!' says Seamus suddenly noticing my presence. 'I was just lettin' this Scotsman of yours have a taste of our best Irish whiskey. Can I get you a glass darlin'?'

'That's very kind of you but I'll give it a miss I think Seamus. I'm not a big whiskey drinker,' I reply already worried about where this session is heading.

'Oh go on now, you can't be saying no to an Irishman. Just a small one. Here, I'll get you a glass, come and sit down.' And with that Seamus weaves his way to the dresser and lifts down another tumbler. 'Here you are now, tell me what you make of that,' he says pouring me a large measure and waiting for me to take a sip.

'Mmm, you can certainly feel it go down,' I reply as the alcohol clears my sinuses and finds its way warmly down to my stomach.

'Well this is a Pearse whiskey Christine, it's a five year-old blend. You can smell the smoke can you not?'

'I think it's more sort of honey and, let me see, vanilla,' I reply, savouring the next mouthful.

'She's got a good palate this woman of yours Rob!' exclaims Seamus excitedly. 'Wait there you two because I've got something even more special in the cab,' he says, heaving himself up from his chair and disappearing into the hall. Cha-Cha is straight out of her basket and about to run after him when I manage to scoop her up. A few moments later the front door opens and our lodger returns with another bottle which he plonks on the table and uncorks the top.

'Seven year Distiller's Choice, oh you're going to like this one folks!' he says pouring a measure into our now empty glasses.

I lift the glass and take a sniff before taking a swig and let it swirl round my mouth. 'Christmas cake!' I announce, now feeling quite confident. 'And hints of cinnamon.'

Rob is staring fondly at me with a glazed expression while Seamus is sitting beaming at me, clearly impressed with my appreciation of his favourite tipple.

'To be sure Christine, 'tis an excellent palate you've got. Would you be liking another drop?' he asks reaching for the bottle.

'I think I'd better stop there Seamus or I'm going to be rendered incapable for the rest of the day thanks all the same. Anyhow, let me show you to your room,' I suggest, hoping that managing to remove him from the kitchen will put an end to the drinking spree.

'Oh don't be worrying yourself darlin', I know me way. Anyhow, thank you for accommodating me and I'm sorry for landin' on you like this. I'll head upstairs and drop me things off and then pop into town for the afternoon. I won't be too late back so don't you worry.' And with that he heads for the door and disappears upstairs.

'Well that's a relief darling,' I whisper, turning back to Rob, but my beloved is fast asleep at the table with his head on his arms.

The afternoon passes quietly. I take Cha-Cha out into the garden where she runs around under the trees barking at falling leaves and trying to catch them as they spin to the ground. Her silky fur gets ruffled by the wind and she tries in vain to catch her tail, spinning round in circles and yapping furiously. It's hard to believe that one so tiny can be so fierce.

'Come on then Cha-Cha, in we go,' I shout across the garden. She stops, looks at me playfully then shoots off into the shrubbery. 'Cha-Cha!' I call, but she's nowhere to be seen. I head towards the shrubs only for her to dart out and shoot into the house through the back door. As I enter the kitchen Rob is raising his head off the table looking a little worse for wear.

'Oh, hello darling. Er, what time is it?' he asks, looking up from the table.

'Five o'clock,' I reply, looking at my watch.

'Five? What happened to the day?'

'Well you slept through most of it.'

'Oh Chris I'm so sorry. It must have been the whiskey,' he says apologetically, ruffling his hair with his hands. 'Did I have any lunch?'

'No, you've been out for the count since Seamus went into town which was about three hours ago.'

'Three hours? I've slept for three hours?'

'Afraid so. How's your head?'

'I don't know, I haven't asked it yet.'

'Do you want something to eat? You must be hungry.'

'I am but I don't know what I fancy.'

'I could do you a fry-up, sausage, bacon, beans, black pudding, eggs, mushrooms …'

Rob is suddenly on his feet and heading for the downstairs

loo. He emerges a few minutes later looking distinctly ashen.

'Mmm, I think that maybe you need to go and lie down again,' I suggest. 'I'll take Cha-Cha out for a walk and give you a shout when we get back.'

'Alright darling. I think that's a good idea. I should have known better than to let Seamus persuade me to drink so much. I will go and lie down for a while if you don't mind.' And so he heads off up the stairs.

Cha-Cha and I enjoy a walk around the local area where I look enviously at some of the many red-brick villas. The Victorians really knew how to build houses. Unlike the mass building projects of the sixties and seventies these houses were built to last, even if they do prove to be a bit big and draughty inside. Many of them have been turned into apartments or guest houses as the majority of them are too large for the modern family. Gone are the days of having seven children and a couple of servants. We meet several dog-walkers who either give us a wide birth or laugh as their own dog has a sniff at Cha-Cha who has to give them what for. Every dog seems big compared to her but they are all totally intimidated by her. We wend our way back to the house where Rob is still nowhere to be seen.

'I think it's about time you had a good brush,' I say to Cha-Cha who cocks her head on one side and looks at me enquiringly. I go to the drawer where her things are kept and, taking out her brush, kneel down to remove her coat but she's having none of it. The brush becomes her mortal enemy and, before I have time to react, she's got it in her jaws and has run off out of the kitchen and into the sitting-room. I follow her only to find her hiding behind the settee, still with the brush in her mouth and growling. I decide to leave her alone rather than try to retrieve it and head back to the kitchen where I settle down with a book.

It's early evening by the time Rob reappears but he does look a great deal better than he did earlier.

'Feeling better darling?' I ask.

'Yes thank you love. I'm sorry about earlier. Is it time for dinner? I'm feeling quite hungry.'

'I can get started if you like, I thought we'd just have some fish and salad if that's okay with you? I didn't think you'd want anything heavy.'

'Oh good thinking. Yes, that would be fine thank you love,' replies Rob settling down on a kitchen chair. 'I wonder what time our guest will be back?'

'Ha! He must have heard you. I think that's him now,' I reply, as the front door opens. Immediately a strong smell of curry emanates from the hallway as Seamus removes his coat and comes into the kitchen.

'Good evening folks! I hope you don't mind but I bought myself a carry-out. Betty doesn't mind if I eat here in the evening as long as I feed myself. I couldn't resist a vindaloo from the Indian place down the road, they do a really grand one,' he says, grabbing a plate from the dresser. My heart sinks as he proceeds to delve into his take-away carrier-bag, removing a series of small foil dishes and then their lids, exposing a selection of garishly-coloured dishes before transferring spoonfuls of the greasy sauces to his plate.

'Would you like to try some you two? There's plenty here if you'd like some,' he says, tearing off a large piece of naan bread and dipping it into the sauce.

'That's very kind of you Seamus but I was just about to cook our own meal. You enjoy your curry and I'll get on with ours if you don't mind.'

It's a little later in the evening, dinner over and the kitchen and nearby rooms still stinking of curry, that I decide to go and have a bath and an early night. I can't help thinking that we should now be waiting for Rod to come on stage. He'll probably be singing my favourite songs from The American Songbook. The very thought of Maggie May makes me yearn for the old discos, us all punching the air and lifting the roof off. The fact that we've lost money on two expensive tickets does little to cheer my mood.

It takes forever for the bath to fill, it's a huge, cast iron affair so the temperature of the water is immediately lowered considerably the minute it leaves the tap. There's a bottle of bubbles on the shelf next to the bath so I tip some in to make the experience a little more luxurious. I climb in and wallow for a while, reflecting on our stay. It's certainly been eventful that's for sure. At least it'll just be the two of us after tomorrow's breakfast.

I realise that I'm beginning to go wrinkly so haul myself out of the bath, slip on my pyjamas and dressing-gown and head downstairs to say goodnight to the men. It's just as I approach the sitting-room door that I can hear Seamus's voice.

'There, now do you see what I mean Robbie? There's just that little hint of spearmint and then honey. Pure nectar don't you think?'

On opening the door my suspicions are confirmed. The pair of them are sitting by the fire, tumblers in hand with a half-empty bottle on the table.

'Oh hello Christine! I was just letting Rob have a taste of the top of the range. They only made nine hundred bottles of this stuff, it's like liquid satin. Would you like to try a drop?'

'No thank you Seamus, I think I'll head for bed,' I reply tersely, glaring at Rob. 'What time would you like breakfast?'

'Well if it's not too early for you I'll need to be on the road by half past seven so would seven be okay?'

'Fine,' I reply, quietly thinking the sooner that this man leaves the better. 'I'll see you in the morning. Goodnight.'

'Good night,' they chorus, each raising a glass in my direction as I stomp off upstairs.

I have no idea what time it is when the bedroom door creaks open and Rob attempts to tiptoe through to the bathroom. I'm determined not to speak to him as I'm quietly fuming. How he can have been stupid enough to enter into another drinking bout is beyond me. I bury my head under the covers and ignore the noises that are coming from the bathroom. He's even singing damn him. His isn't the most tuneful voice at the best of times but for some reason he manages to stay in the same key when he's had too much to drink.

Having finished in the bathroom he turns out the light and tries to find his way to the bed. He's clearly lost his way when suddenly there's a mighty crash as he walks into what I assume is the wardrobe door. There's a loud cry of pain followed by some cursing and then the singing resumes. I can sense him wrestling with the bed-clothes as he attempts to climb into bed. The smell of whiskey is overpowering as he gets under the duvet and wriggles his way over to my side of the bed but I lie ram-rod straight still determined to ignore him. The singing continues as he wraps himself around me.

'If you want my body and you think I'm sexy, come on, sugar, tell me so,' at which point I can contain myself no longer and snort with laughter.

'God you're impossible Robert Baird. It's a good job I love you.'

'And I love you too me darlin',' he slurs falling instantly to sleep.

THE NAKED TRUTH

'SO WHAT'S ON THE agenda?' asks Rob one morning at breakfast.

'Do you mean today?' I reply looking up from the crossword.

'No, I mean where are we going next? I'm getting withdrawal symptoms.'

'Oh, I see. Well I've got three applications in but I haven't heard back from any of them.'

'Mmm, so where are they?' comes back the mumbled reply through a mouthful of toast.

'Denmark, Barcelona and Munich.'

'Blimey, you've picked an interesting range there. Any preference?'

'Well to be honest I'm getting a bit twitchy about the Danish one.'

'Why's that?' asks Rob pouring us both another cup of coffee.

'The owners just seem too finicky for my liking. The list of 'duties' as they call them is ridiculous.'

'Such as?'

'Well they want the grass cut regularly, the leaves brushed off the patio, the roses dead-headed, and wait for this! They want the sitters to send regular photos of the vegetable garden.'

'Good grief, what on earth for?'

'I suppose they just want reassurance that it's being looked after.'

'Mmm, I see what you mean. But we can always say no if they do choose us.'

'That's true. It's a pity though, it sounded really lovely otherwise.'

'So what about Munich? I've always fancied visiting Germany, it's somewhere I've never been. All that beer and Brunhildas.'

'Yes, me too, but they're a very young couple and I'm

beginning to think that youngsters don't tend to go for old wrinklies like us.'

'Well more fool them. We're not exactly going to be having wild parties are we, or going off clubbing and neglecting the animals?'

'No, but it does seem to be the way of things. We'll just have to keep our fingers crossed. Maybe we'll hit lucky with Barcelona. I've always wanted to see the architecture there. That would be my favourite choice. Anyhow, we'll just have to wait and see.'

It's with more than a little surprise that we get a message in our mailbox the following morning asking if we'd still be interested in going to Munich. Having given up hope of getting anywhere with that particular advert we're more than a little excited.

'Well that proves me wrong Rob. I really didn't think we stood a chance of being chosen. They'd had lots of applications. Maybe we're not so useless after all?'

'I should think not. We older folk are more experienced and reliable, I reckon we make an excellent choice. So remind me, what am I letting myself in for?'

'It's a dog,' I reply, bringing up the original advert on the iPad.

'Yes, but what sort of a dog?'

'A grumpy one by the look of things.'

'What do you mean grumpy? Let me have a look,' says Rob, coming to look over my shoulder. 'Oh my goodness you're right! What a face.' We're looking at a miniature Schnauzer who's scowling into the camera, his bushy eye-brows over-hanging a very severe stare. 'He's got a magnificent beard though, I'm quite jealous,' says Rob, stroking his newly-trimmed stubble. 'What's his name?'

'Manfred.'

'Good grief. Still, I suppose he is German. Do you suppose he speaks German?'

'Well of course he does. You can't expect him to understand English but I'm sure we'd manage.'

'But we won't need to be able to say anything will we? I mean everyone speaks English these days.'

'I hope we don't, but I might do a bit of school-girl revision. It's important to be able to say please and thank you and ask for things. There might still be some vocabulary lurking at the back of my memory.'

'Of course, I'd forgotten you'd learned German for a while.'

'Yes, but only for a year and I did tell you that was rather a long time ago. I doubt I can remember anything now. How's about, "*Wo ist die Katze? Die Katze ist im Kleiderschrank.*"'

'So what does that mean?'

'Where is the cat? The cat is in the wardrobe.'

'Well that should come in handy. Don't you know anything useful like, "a glass of red wine and a pint of lager"?'

'I can manage the wine but not the lager I'm afraid. And they drink litres not pints.'

'Alright clever-clogs. So, are we going to accept?'

'I don't see why not, it's better than sitting at home. I'll drop them a line now.'

Our new home is listed as an apartment with a small garden on the edge of the area known as the Englischer Garten, a huge, sprawling park that winds its way right through the city. With both the park and the city on our doorstep there's no need for a car which is always our preference as driving in foreign cities can prove quite hair-raising, especially in a left-hand drive on the wrong side of the road. The idea of being able to take Manfred for his walks without having to negotiate busy streets is particularly appealing. The owners, a young couple called Max and Ingrid, are apparently heading to Italy for a friend's big birthday and will be leaving in the early evening on the day of our arrival.

Following a flight direct to Munich airport we take the shuttle-bus to the station where a taxi seems to be the easiest solution. I show the driver the address and within a short drive we arrive at Begonienstraße where he pulls up in front of a large, white house with a red, pan-tiled roof.

'This looks like us,' I call to Rob who's struggling with his suitcase. 'Can you manage that thing?'

'Yes, it's just a bit awkward, that's all.'

'Well you can't give me the excuse that it's winter and it's full of thick clothes this time. It's mid-summer and all you need is a couple of pairs of shorts and a few t-shirts.'

'And a smart shirt and a couple of pairs of chinos and my sandals and my reading-material and my toiletries. Anyhow, are you going to ring this doorbell or not?'

I look for the name next to the number and ring the bell, already feeling a little anxious about meeting the owners. There's no sign of any movement so I ring again. Still no one comes to the door.

'Are you sure it's the right apartment Chris?'

'Yes, of course I am. It's got their name on it and it's the right number. Maybe the bell's not working?'

'Well, I suppose it's possible. Here, let me have a look. What did you say the name was?'

'Zimmermann.'

'Mmmm, yes it seems to be the right one. Maybe they're in the garden? I'll walk round the side and see if anyone's there. Nope,' he says, returning to the front door, 'no sign of anyone.'

It's just as we're wondering quite what we should do that a couple appear in the distance running down the road towards us carrying a large surfboard between them. They're both wearing swimming gear and are clearly out of breath. As they approach we realise that they're both absolutely soaked, their hair hanging limply in rats' tails. They slow down on reaching the gate and stagger up the path to where we're standing.

'*Es tut mir so leid, dass wir zu spät sind. Wir surften auf dem Fluss und ich habe mein Board verloren*,' pants the girl looking flirtatiously at the boy whom we assume to be Max and giggling. We smile back awkwardly.

'What did she say?' mutters Rob behind his hand.

'I haven't a clue,' I reply.

'*Bitte, komm 'rein. Kann ich deine Tasche für dich nehmen?*' asks Max, gesturing to Rob that he will take his bag and leading us into the house.

'Thank you,' replies Rob. 'Er, *Dankeschön.*'

'*Bitteschön*,' replies Max, smiling at Rob's attempt to say thank you. '*Möchten Sie eine Tasse Kaffee oder ein Bier? Es ist so heiß heute.*'

'*Ja danke. Zwei Kaffee bitte*,' I reply in my best German. I'm already thinking that the sooner these two leave the better or the conversation is going to be very limited.

Having been shown to our room we take a few things out of our cases and have a shower, change into more comfortable clothes and venture downstairs to the kitchen where we perch on a stool each next to the breakfast bar. There's nobody around and what is more puzzling is that there is no sign of Manfred. We can hear footsteps coming down the stairs and Max appears dressed in what we assume to be his travelling gear, a pair of track-suit bottoms and a t-shirt. He's a good-looking young man, probably in his late twenties, with a mop of curly, blonde hair and the bluest of eyes, he looks every inch the blonde Adonis.

'Er, Max, *wo ist Manfred?*' I ask tentatively.

'*Ach ja, Manfred. Er ist nicht hier. Er bleibt bei meiner Mutter. Sie wird ihn morgen früh nach Hause bringen. Es tut mir leid, ich hätte es Ihnen sagen sollen.*'

I've managed to grasp the fact that Manfred is, in fact, not here. If I've understood correctly the message is that Max's mother is going to be bringing him over tomorrow but I might have got that wrong. Max disappears into the next room and returns with a file that contains all the information for our stay. Fortunately it's in English so at least we have all the essential information that we need. As we're leafing through the pages Ingrid arrives looking quite different, her hair now hanging in blonde curls and her face made up. She puts her suitcase next to Max's in the hall and smiles nervously at us. We're both stuck for conversation.

'*Wir haben eine Katze,*' I say turning to Ingrid.

'*Ach, das ist schön. Wie heißt sie?*' she asks.

Damn, I never considered that she might reply. I'm now madly trying to think of a name for the cat that we haven't got. 'Er, Tigger,' I reply.

'*Das ist ein guter Name,*' she says, laughing.

I'm hugely relieved when Max arrives with his case and, glancing at his watch, suggests to Ingrid that they had better get moving. We walk to the end of the path with them where they climb into a lovely old VW Beetle.

'*Auf Wiedersehen!*' calls Rob. '*Bon voyage!*' and with that the Beetle speeds off down the street. 'Well thank goodness that's over Chris. It could have got very awkward. I never thought for a moment that they wouldn't speak English.'

'No, nor me. All the communication has been in English, but maybe they used Google Translate, so many people do.'

'And what's all this about us having a cat if I understood your conversation with Ingrid correctly?'

'I know. I was just desperate to break the silence and I couldn't think of any other phrases. It doesn't matter, they're hardly likely to want to know about it.'

'Well let's hope that Max's mother speaks some English when she arrives tomorrow or there could be another embarrassing silence.'

It's about ten o'clock the following morning when the door-bell rings.

'That must be her,' says Rob. 'You'd better go Chris.'

On opening the door I'm greeted by a rather severe-looking woman, probably in her early fifties, with beautifully coiffured auburn hair. She's quite portly and is wearing a smart summer dress and carrying a fan. Manfred is pulling on his lead, eager to investigate his visitors.

'Er, *Guten Morgen*,' I say, holding out my hand in greeting.

'Oh you needn't worry about that *Guten Morgen* rubbish. I'm English for God's sake, born in Bath and brought up in the Cotswolds. So remind me, what's your name?' she asks rather brusquely in a decidedly plummy accent.

'I'm Christine and this is my husband Robert,' I reply, turning to introduce Rob. 'Please, do come in.'

'No need to invite me into my own son's home for heaven's sake.'

'And this must be Manfred,' says Rob, crouching down to let Manfred sniff his hand. 'He's a cute little fellow aren't you boy?'

'Damned nuisance if you ask me,' our visitor says curtly. 'Why on earth they got a dog is beyond me. They're both busy working so guess who ends up doing all the walks?'

'We never had a chance to ask Max and Ingrid what they do,' I say leading the way through to the sitting-room.

'Ingrid works at the Tourist Information Centre and Max is a radio presenter for Bayern 1,' she says settling down in a chair. 'Any chance of a coffee? I'm in need of reviving after that walk.'

'Of course, I'll go and make one now,' I reply, heading for the kitchen. So if Ingrid works in tourism and Max has an English mother how come they neither of them spoke English to us I wonder? I make us all a coffee and head back to the sitting-room where Rob is being his charming self. Mrs Zimmermann has clearly thawed and her voice seems to have mellowed.

'Ah, I see,' says Rob. 'So he finished his degree in England before coming back to Germany?'

'Yes, his father and I divorced just as Max was leaving school so it made sense for us to go back to England where I had family and Max could improve his English, although to be honest he was already pretty fluent having been brought up by an English mother. Ah, thank you my dear,' she says, taking the cup of coffee from me.

So for some reason Max and Ingrid had chosen to let us muddle our way through with our limited German whilst quietly having a good laugh, no doubt.

'So does Max have his own programme or is he a producer?' I ask, determined to unravel the mystery.

'Yes, he has a regular afternoon slot, mainly music but with a sort of radio version of candid camera where he plays tricks on people. He has a terrible sense of humour, he always has, ever since he was a child, but it seems to be very popular with his listeners.'

It's all beginning to make sense now but I'm quietly annoyed that he and Ingrid should consider it appropriate to play a practical joke on us. I'm tempted to let his mother know what has happened but think better of saying anything.

'So what made you come back to Germany?' I ask.

'Well Max wanted to come back as it was where his friends were and he'd already met Ingrid. They got married shortly after he came back and I was hoping there might be grandchildren at some point. Still, I live in hope. Anyhow, I'll love you and leave you,' she smiles, finishing her coffee and heaving herself up out of the chair. 'He'll be fine,' she says looking at Manfred who's already settled down on the sofa. 'He's a good-natured dog, he won't be any trouble. I'm going away myself tomorrow for a couple of days but only into the country so I won't be too far away. I'm sure Max has left you my contact details,' she says, picking up her fan. 'Bye bye Manfred, you be a good boy,' she calls back as I show her to the front door. 'Goodbye, nice to meet you both.'

'So the pair of them speak perfect English!' I fume. 'What a dreadful thing to do to someone, leaving us struggling. I'm sure they both had a jolly good laugh.'

'I agree, it was a bit off,' says Rob going to inspect Manfred.

'A bit off? It was bloody rude Rob. I am so angry.'

'It does make you think though doesn't it?'

'What does?' I snap trying to calm myself.

'Well, how we always expect everyone to speak our language. I mean why should they?'

'Because it's the second language in Europe and most people outside the UK are taught to speak it,' I reply abruptly.

'I know you're always keen to make an effort with other people's languages, but English folk aren't going to learn Dutch or Norwegian unless they have a real need for it. I mean we all learn French because it's more widely spoken than German.'

'Yes, but the point I'm trying to make is that if I could speak fluent German I wouldn't sit back and let a German make a fool of himself trying to speak English. Anyhow, let's forget about it. I'd quite like to enjoy the rest of my stay.'

The following morning Manfred wakes us early with his continuous barking. I crawl out of bed and let him out into the garden while I prepare his breakfast. The day is already warm and destined to get hotter. I wander out into the garden in my bare feet which Manfred thinks is great fun as he starts diving at my toes and trying to bite them.

'*Nein Manfred!* Stop it!,' I cry, trying to get out of his reach, but the more I attempt to stop him, the more he thinks it's a good game. I quickly put his food bowl down in the kitchen and take myself back to the bedroom to get changed. 'That dog's a horror Rob! He's just been trying to nip my toes. We'll need to get him out early before it gets too hot. How's about we have some breakfast and then go and explore the Englischer Garten?'

'Good idea, I'll go and make the coffee,' says Rob reaching for his dressing-gown.

The Englischer Garten proves to be much bigger than we'd imagined with vast expanses of open meadows planted with a huge variety of mature trees. The park is divided into several areas by the river Isar and its tributaries, some of which come together to form a huge lake. It all seems very popular with the locals who walk, jog, cycle, exercise their dogs or sit watching the world go by. Manfred clearly loves the place and trots along sniffing in the long grass and snuffling in the bushes. He's well-behaved with other dogs which is a bonus, but we don't feel inclined to let him off his lead. The information that Max and Ingrid have left for us suggests that if he gets the scent of something, like most terriers, his recall is hopeless. The idea of losing him in such a vast area doesn't bear thinking about so we compromise by keeping him on a long lead.

Although it's cloudy, it's still very warm and slightly muggy. There are plenty of people about and we meander along the many paths that wind their way through the parkland, admiring the huge variety of trees and enjoying the river. Following a path that seems less well-trodden, we stumble across what seems to be almost a small village of huts which we assume to be allotments. However, on closer inspection we discover that it's actually a community of bee-keepers who keep hives there and grow plant varieties that the bees will feed on. There are small stalls outside the various huts selling lots of different products made from beeswax as well as jars of honey.

'Oh what a lovely idea Chris!' exclaims Rob. Manfred seems keen to take a look too and stands with his paws against the fence trying to peer into the gardens. 'Now you be careful, we don't want you getting stung!' laughs Rob, pulling gently on the lead to remove Manfred's nose from the flowers. 'Let's go down by the river, it'll be cooler there.'

We follow a path down to the riverbank and can feel the change in temperature already.

'This is one of the things I really do miss at home Rob, not having any rivers. There's something very relaxing about water and it's so beautifully clean here too.'

'Yes, I know what you mean, and the wildlife is so interesting too. Oh my, look ahead Chris!'

Heading towards us is a veritable army of sausage-dogs, five to be exact. They're being walked by a young woman who is looking slightly stressed. Although she's got them on leads that tether them in groups, her task is anything but easy as they all seem to want to go in different directions. Manfred doesn't seem in the least bit interested even when one jumps in his direction yapping furiously. The woman looks suitably embarrassed and tries to unravel the knot that they've created only succeeding in making things worse.

'Here, you take Manfred and I'll see if I can help,' says Rob, immediately moving in to play the good Samaritan. By taking one of the leads he manages to restore some degree of order and hands it back with a smile.

'*Dankeschön*,' smiles back the young lady, clearly grateful for the assistance.

'*Bitteschön*,' replies Rob, much to my surprise, giving a little wave to the party as they head on up the path.

'Well, you're becoming quite the linguist aren't you?' I tease. 'At this rate I'll be able to send you out to do the shopping on your own.'

It isn't quite how it works out when, the following day, I realise that we're in need of a few things from the supermarket.

'Well I'm happy to take Manfred out if you want to go and do the shopping Chris, then we've got more of the day to explore.'

I have to agree that it's better that I do the shopping as I'm also the chief cook, but there's the usual concern regarding Rob's sense of direction. The park is one of the largest public parks in Europe so goodness knows how I'd find him if he got lost.

'That sounds like a good plan but are you sure you know where you're going? It would be no use ringing me and trying to describe where you were because I'd never find you.'

'Absolutely sweetheart. I'll simply walk him down to the river, over the bridge, round that open area of grass and back home again. I promise I'll be fine. It's probably a good idea if we go now because it feels as though today's going to be a scorcher once this cloud lifts.'

'Alright then, I'll see you back here. Enjoy your walk the pair of you.'

And so, attaching Manfred's lead, man and dog wander off down the road to the park.

The shopping proves a bit of a challenge as my vocabulary is very limited but fortunately there's plenty of pre-packed meat and, needless to say, lots of sausage. I indulge in some small cakes and a bottle of German *Spätburgunder*, a red wine that we've never tried before, as well as buying a few basic provisions. By the time I've finished the bags are quite heavy, and I'm beginning to wonder if I should give in and take a taxi as there are a couple hovering outside. However, I decide to brave it and make my way slowly back to the apartment.

By the time I get back I'm regretting my decision. There's no sign of Rob and Manfred but I try not to worry and busy myself putting the shopping away. To my huge relief it's only a matter of minutes before the pair of them can be heard coming into the garden, Rob talking to Manfred as they come in through the back door.

'*Guter Junge Manfred!* Hello darling, how did you get on?' asks Rob, giving me a peck on the cheek. 'Did you get everything you needed?'

'Yes thanks, as usual I probably bought too much. What

about you? You look a bit flushed. You haven't been charging around have you?'

'No, not at all, but it's really quite hot out there already. I'm glad I got *mein Hund* out for his walk this side of midday.'

'So why this sudden effort to speak German? You've never bothered with languages before?'

'Well I took heed of your good example and just thought it would help Manfred to be more relaxed so I've been learning a few phrases by going on Youtube and using Google Translate. Anyhow, dare I ask what's for lunch *meine liebe Frau?*'

'I got some cold meats, some cheese and some nice rye bread, oh and a bottle of red wine for us to try. I thought that maybe we could leave Manfred here for an hour and go and have a picnic in the Englischer Garten. I'm sure we could find somewhere cool if we go under the shade of the trees or by the lake.'

'That's a splendid idea. I'll just change into my shorts and we can go whenever you're ready.'

'I'm sure it's this way to the lake Rob. We cross this bridge and then follow the other branch of the river until we pass that open grassed area.'

'I hate to disagree but I think it'd be quicker if we stayed on this side of the river and crossed at the next bridge,' he suggests somewhat nervously.

'But we've never been that way, no let's stick to this route, come on,' and I head off across the wooden bridge. 'At least it's cooler here. I certainly wouldn't want to be sitting in the open today, that sun's really fierce.'

'No, you're right. The sooner we get into the shade the better,' replies Rob looking furtively around him.

'Are you alright?' I ask. 'You look very twitchy. Is there something wrong?'

'No, no, nothing's wrong. It's probably the heat getting to me.'

As we follow the path towards the lake there's a sudden cry from the long grass to the right of us.

'*Hallo Robert!*' shouts the voice but Rob walks hurriedly on.

'Rob, there's someone shouting to you,' I call to him.

'There can't be, I don't know anyone,' he says heading off again.

'*Robert! Hallo!*' comes the call again.

I turn in the direction of the voice only to see a young woman waving enthusiastically in his direction. 'It's clearly someone who knows you Rob. Who on earth is it?'

'I have no idea, they must be mistaken. Come on darling, let's move on,' he says taking me by the arm and guiding me along the path.

'*Wo ist Manfred?*' comes another cry from the long grass.

'That woman's just asked where Manfred is, so she must know you.'

'I've told you they must be mistaken Chris. You know I don't know anyone here.'

The young woman is now kneeling in the long grass and waving frantically in our direction and, to my horror, I realise that she's topless.

'*Warum kommst du nicht und setzt dich zu uns?*' she cries.

Rob is clearly embarrassed but I'm beginning to understand his reluctance to acknowledge the young lady who, I now realise, is the damsel in distress with the sausage dogs that he'd rescued yesterday.

'Oh I see,' I say, folding my arms across my chest. 'So when did you bump into her again?'

'Er, this morning when I was walking Manfred. She was sun-bathing here with a girl-friend.'

'And?'

'And nothing.'

'Were they fully clad when you exchanged your *Hallos*?'

'I can't say I noticed.'

'Can't say you noticed? For God's sake Rob she's got boobs on her like Dolly Parton and you say you didn't notice?' I shout. 'So are you going to go and say hello or are we going to stand here like a couple of wallies?'

'Well I don't really know. It's all a bit embarrassing isn't it? It feels very awkward talking to someone who's half-naked. I think we'll give it a miss. Let's just pretend we haven't understood and walk off.'

And so, with a weak smile and a wave we move on in the direction of the lake. There are lots of people seeking shelter under some of the magnificent trees but a good number lying around in the open sun-bathing. As we wander along I realise, on examining them more closely, that many of them are absolutely starkers. Overcome by embarrassment I take Rob by the arm and move him hurriedly along the path.

'What on earth are you doing Chris? Is there something wrong?'

'Yes,' I reply, looking studiously at my feet. 'Half of these people are naked, not just topless but stark naked,' I reply keeping my eyes fixed on the ground while continuing to walk.

'Really?' asks Rob in disbelief stopping dead in his tracks. 'Surely not, isn't it against the law?'

'Clearly not. I know that the Germans have a very relaxed approach to nudity but I didn't think it extended to public spaces.'

'Crikey, you're right. Look at him!' exclaims Rob looking very obviously at a middle-aged man with a large paunch who is arranging a blanket on the grass. 'There are a few blokes here who could do with shedding a few pounds.'

I glance up hesitantly only to spot an elderly couple with more than the odd wrinkle sitting in garden chairs enjoying a picnic.

'Well they all seem very relaxed about it Chris. Maybe we're the ones with the problem. Perhaps we should try and chill, we could sit and have our picnic here if you like?'

'Robert Baird, are you suggesting that I should take all my clothes off and then sit and eat my lunch because I'm telling you now, I will do no such thing. And I'll have you know that I believe in public decency and my body is not for display purposes.'

'But nobody's interested in what you do or what you look like, they don't exactly look like a load of voyeurs do they? If you look around people are just chatting or reading or listening to music or playing on their phones. They're not sitting gawping at people or taking candid photographs now are they?'

'Rob, I have no wish to 'look around' thank you very much. Could we please just head for the lake and a nice, quiet area in the shade?' I snarl.

On eventually finding a relatively quiet spot we sit down on a bench and set the bag of picnic food between us. It's a lot cooler and there's a beautiful view of the water.

'Sausage?' asks Rob, poking around in the various bags.

'I don't think so,' I reply curtly.

'They like their sausages don't they?'

'Yes, clearly, but I think I'll just have a ham sandwich,' I reply, setting a sandwich down on the tea-towel between us.

There's a sudden scream from behind us and a woman crying out, '*Nein Arno! Herkommen! Lass es! Arno!*' at which point a young Labrador sticks its head through the back of the bench and grabs my sandwich in one mouthful. Arno's owner is suitably embarrassed and rushes up to catch him and to apologise. '*Es tut mir so leid.*'

'Don't worry,' I say smiling reassuringly, but the poor woman is beside herself. She grabs hold of Arno and quickly attaches his lead before dragging him off across the grass.

'Well if that was my lunch I guess I've had it,' I sigh.

'Are you sure you don't want a bite of my sausage?' asks Rob.

'No thank you, I'll wait until we get back and have something then,' I reply, leaning back on the bench.

'Maybe we should get back to Manfred Chris? He's been on his own for over an hour.'

'Fine, let's make a move, only could we avoid the naturist colony on the way back?'

'If you know the way, lead on McDuff!'

Manfred is more than happy to see us, in fact he's ecstatic. His little tail wags so fast it becomes a blur. He runs to get a toy for us and then shoots off into the sitting room doing several circuits of the furniture, stopping, changing direction and then shooting off again.

'He's a lovely little fellow isn't he Chris? He's so affectionate, and he's clever. Schnauzers are supposed to be really good at agility.'

'I can imagine that, he's a bright little button, aren't you Manfred?' I croon, bending down to make a fuss of him. 'It seems to be clouding over again. Why don't we take him out for his walk now? We could go over the bridge and head towards the children's play area.'

'Good idea, I'll get his lead. Come on then Manfred, walkies!' As Rob reaches for the lead Manfred is super-excited and keeps leaping in the air on all four paws as though he's got springs on his feet. 'We'll have to give him a brush when we get back, his beard's all soggy and we can't have him looking a mess.'

'Come on then Herr Baird. Let's get this boy out before he does himself a mischief.'

Manfred's a little wary of crossing the bridge as there are big gaps between some of the planks so Rob scoops him up and, in doing so, gets his face licked as a thank you.

'Oh bless him, he's such a sweetheart. I've really fallen for him,' I say, walking alongside Rob and stroking Manfred's head. 'He's even got a little smile when he's happy.'

As we reach the far bank Rob puts him back down and we head for the children's play area. There are several families out with the children all playing happily together. We pass a few people out walking their dogs and a lot of cyclists but the paths are wide enough to accommodate everyone.

'Look Chris!' shouts Rob suddenly, pointing up into a nearby tree, 'a squirrel, but it's black!'

'Oh wow! I didn't know you could get black squirrels.' I'm surprised that Manfred isn't barking but as I turn round to see what he's up to I can see him chewing. 'What have you got?' I shout, suddenly panicked that he might have something in his mouth that could choke him. I run up to him and bend down to try to open his mouth. There's no sign of anything so whatever he found has been swallowed.

'I wonder what he found?' quizzes Rob, looking around for further evidence. 'It could be anything in this area, I mean the kids are probably throwing bits of sandwich around or dropping sweets.'

'Yes, but we wouldn't want him to have a chicken bone or anything that might choke him.'

'Well he seems to be okay,' says Rob, bending down to stroke Manfred's head. 'Hang on a minute though, what's that?' he asks. 'It looks like a raisin.'

'God I hope not.'

'It is Chris, in fact there's a huge pile of them here in the grass.'

'Oh no! That must have been what he was eating.'

'Well we can't be sure but it would seem the obvious answer.'

'Yes, and we can't risk taking any chances. We need to get him to a vet straight away.'

'Really? Can't we wait for a bit and see how he is?'

'Absolutely not, they can be fatal in a very short time. We need to find a taxi quickly.'

'Okay, if you say so, I'll carry him, you lead the way.'

Fortunately I always carry the emergency details with us whenever we go out, so I have the vet's telephone number and address on my phone. As we head back towards the road I call the vet, praying that they speak English. To my relief they answer quickly and I'm able to ask in my best school-girl German if there is anyone who speaks English. We're in luck as the girl who I'm talking to speaks our language perfectly. I explain the situation as we head towards the taxi-rank beside the shopping precinct, Rob beginning to struggle in the heat. The vet wants to know how quickly we can get Manfred to them.

'I think in half an hour,' I reply, my voice beginning to wobble with the anxiety. She makes it quite clear that we need to be quick.

'I really didn't realise that it was this serious Chris,' pants Rob as we run to the nearest taxi. The driver gets out to greet us but looks dubiously at Manfred.

'*Mein Hund ist krank,*' I cry, looking anxiously into the driver's eyes. '*Wir müssen zum Doktor gehen. Schnell.*'

'*Haben sie die Adresse?*'

'*Ja!*'

'*Bitte,*' he smiles, opening the cab door.

The three of us pile into the back seats, Rob still cradling Manfred.

'I saw him chewing something Rob so he must have had a couple at least. Oh God, I just hope he's going to be alright.'

'You did incredibly well with your German darling. Where did all that come from?'

'Some distant memory of fifty years ago. I didn't even know I had that vocabulary, except I had to say doctor because I don't know the German for vet.'

'Well, well done you. Let's hope he hasn't eaten too many raisins.'

'I'm sure I've read that a dog can have renal failure after only eating a couple and it doesn't even matter what size the dog is. Oh Rob, pray he's going to be alright!'

Some twenty minutes later the driver pulls up outside the vet's and, leaving Rob to settle the fare, I take Manfred off him and run into the surgery. There's already someone waiting for us.

'Hello, can you bring him in here?' asks the tall blonde woman, smiling reassuringly. She's a well-built girl probably in her late twenties. 'So how long ago did he have the raisins and how many?'

'About twenty minutes ago but I don't know how many he ate, I think only a few.'

'Okay, so I need to weigh him and then I'm going to give him an injection to make him sick.'

'Of course,' I reply, trying to hold back the tears. We pop poor Manfred on the scales and then lift him onto the steel table.

'If you can just hold him still?' she asks and gently inserts a needle into the scruff of his neck. 'There we go. If you can stay here with him and I'll come and check on you later.'

As she leaves the room Rob arrives looking suitably worried. At the same time poor Manfred throws up on the floor. It doesn't look good.

'Well, he clearly had more than we thought,' I say, bending over to examine the regurgitated contents of his stomach. 'There must be at least a dozen in there Rob.'

'Thank goodness you knew what to do Chris. I would have waited to see how he was later.'

'And later could have been too late. Anyhow, the important thing is we got him here quickly. I just feel so sorry for him having to go through this.'

No sooner have the words left my mouth than poor Manfred's sides start to heave and he's horribly sick again. As the vet wants to inspect the damage we can't even clean up after him.

'Oh he looks so sorry for himself poor fellow. But I wonder where the raisins came from Chris? I suppose it could have been kids throwing them away or spilling them?'

'I hate to say it but I think it was deliberate. There were too many for it to have been a casual spillage. There were easily a couple of big handfuls, if not more. I didn't stop to investigate when I realised what had happened.'

'But why would anyone do a thing like that?'

'Because some people hate dogs and some people are just plain wicked. Think of the cases we've read about in England where dogs who've been running round the park have been enticed by something tasty wrapped round something hazardous. Those aren't accidents Rob, they're deliberate attempts to cause an animal serious injury. I don't even like to think about it. No, we were too far away from the children's play area for it to have been an accident.'

There's another great heave as Manfred is sick again. Fortunately there don't seem to be any more raisins but a lot of bile and the remains of his breakfast. I bend down to comfort him just as the vet returns.

'So how is he doing? Mmmm, it looks as though he ate quite a few. You were lucky to get him here so quickly, another few minutes and we might not have been able to save him.' I wince visibly and she leans over to stroke my arm. 'But he's going to be okay. We'll give him a few more minutes until he's got an empty stomach and then I'll give him another injection to stop him being sick.' And at that she smiles reassuringly and disappears again.

'It couldn't be worse could it darling?' remarks Rob, putting his arm round me reassuringly. 'Looking after someone else's animal is such a responsibility. Thank goodness he's going to be alright.'

'Yes, it's fine until something like this happens. And we're going to have to tell Max and Ingrid. I realise that but we're going to have to choose our moment. We don't want to ruin their day and I think today was the birthday party. Once we know that Manfred's out of the woods then I think we could safely leave it until tomorrow.'

Our lovely vet returns and, after giving the patient another injection assures us that Manfred will be fine and that we can take him home.

'Do you know if the owners have an account with us?' she asks as we go back to the reception area.

'According to the notes they left us then yes,' I reply. 'The name is Zimmermann.'

On hearing the name she looks back at me laughing. 'You don't mean Max Zimmermann the radio presenter?'

'Yes, he's the one according to his mother,' I reply.

'I should have realised before, he talks about Manfred a lot on the radio. He's a terrible practical joker. Anyhow, don't worry, we'll put the treatment on his account so you don't have to pay us. The girl at the desk is calling a taxi for you, it should be here any minute. Well goodbye little man,' she says, bending over and stroking Manfred. I'm amazed he doesn't growl at her given the treatment he's had to suffer today.

'Thank you so much,' Rob replies shaking her hand. 'We can't thank you enough.'

'Before we go,' I interrupt, 'can I be cheeky and ask how you speak such good English?It's hard to believe you're German.'

'I learned at school and then I worked in an office where we were all expected to speak nothing but English for one hour every day. Most people here have it as a second language. And thank you for the compliment!'

And so we wander out into the fresh air and breathe a sigh of relief. Manfred seems totally unfazed by his experience and wanders around, nose to the ground having a good sniff. Within only a few minutes our taxi draws up and we pile into the back, Rob hugging Manfred who is resting his chin on Rob's shoulder.

'Well what a relief Rob, I hope we never have to go through that again. I think we're going to need a glass of wine when we get back.'

'Too right and well done you for knowing what to do. I'm still shocked to think it was deliberate.'

'That's a point. When we get back I must make a notice and take it to the park. I'd hate to think that anyone else's dog could suffer the same fate. If you had a dog off the lead it could be fatal. Some dog-walkers wouldn't even know that the dog had eaten anything.'

'That's good thinking Chris. I'll give you a hand as soon as we get back.'

And so, after doing a quick search on Google Translate I head back to the children's play area with a warning sign written in large letters on a piece of cardboard and attached to a stick. I just hope that my translation is near enough to get the message across: '*Achtung! Hundebesitzer! Im Gras sind Rosinen! Für Hunde sind sie giftig.*' Fortunately I have a good idea where to find the raisins and, after a bit of searching, find the spot. I push the stick into the ground and, before leaving attempt to gather up as many of the raisins as I can. I manage to collect two large handfuls and even then I can still see some here and there in the grass. Just as I'm leaving an elderly lady comes walking along with a Yorkshire Terrier so I approach her and point to the sign. She turns to thank me so I'm reassured that the sign says what I wanted it to say.

'Right! Job done!' I cry as I walk through the garden gate. Rob is already reclining on a sun-lounger, a glass of wine by his side. 'You didn't waste any time,' I remark, 'and I'm pleased to note that you kept your shorts on. I don't want these Germans giving you any ideas.'

'Well I did think about stripping off it but I wouldn't want to get my bits burnt!' he laughs.

'We're going to have to let Max and Ingrid know what's happened fairly soon and prepare them for the fact that they're coming home to a bill from the vet,' I say, standing over Rob and blocking the sun.

'I've been thinking that maybe it would be easier to let his mother know. After all we do have the excuse that we didn't think he could speak English and we wouldn't have been able to explain in German,' he says, leaning over and taking a sip of wine.

'Oh good thinking! That's a brilliant idea. We've got her number in the information pack.'

'So why don't you call her now Chris, then she can get in touch with Max and let them know what's happened?'

'Why me? You're the one who seems to have charmed her. I think you should ring,' I reply, settling down on the sun-lounger.

'Oh alright, I suppose it's a fair division of labours after all that you've done today,' he agrees, heading into the house.

Manfred has settled down in the shade and seems to have recovered from his ordeal. It's wonderful to be able to relax after the stress of the day's events. A few minutes later Rob returns with a satisfied smile on his face.

'Well?' I ask, keen to know the outcome.

'Well she was eternally grateful but absolutely horrified when I explained the language barrier with her son. I think he might be in for an earful.'

'He jolly well deserves it after the way he behaved. She must have been quite taken aback. It'll be interesting to see if he contacts us when he realises we know what he was up to.'

It's the following morning, just after getting back from our walk, when the doorbell rings.

'You'd better go Chris in case you need to speak German.'

'On my way,' I call and head for the front door. There's a delivery van outside and a man who is carrying what appears to be a heavy box is struggling up the path.'

'*Frau Baird?*' he enquires.

'*Ja,*' I reply, a little puzzled as we are obviously not expecting anything, but with that he sets the box down on the doorstep and walks off back to the van. I give Rob a shout as I don't think I'm going to be able to lift the box on my own.

'Whatever is it?' he asks. 'Something for Max and Ingrid I assume?'

'No, it's for us but I'm very confused. I mean we haven't ordered anything.'

'Well let's get it inside and see,' says Rob, taking one end and helping me to carry it into the house. 'It's bloomin' heavy that's for sure.'

We both set to to open the box and, on revealing the contents, stop in amazement and gawp at one another.

'Is this from who I think it is?' asks Rob, staring incredulously at twelve bottles of wine.

'I have no idea but I can't imagine who else would be sending us a gift. Isn't there a delivery note?'

'I can't see one. No, hang on a minute, what's this?' he says, removing a piece of paper from the lid of the box and unfolding it. 'Yes, there is a message and it is from Max as anticipated.'

'So, what does it say?'

'Well, you'll be pleased to know that it's in English. And it says: "Dear Christine and Robert, my mother called us last night to tell us that you had had to take Manfred to the vet. We can't thank you enough for acting so quickly as by doing so you saved his life. I have to apologise for the discourteous trick I played when we met. It was very wrong of me and now I feel even worse knowing what you did for us and, of course, for Manfred. I hope you will accept the wine as a small token of our appreciation and trust that you enjoy the rest of your stay. With best wishes and humble apologies, Max and Ingrid." Well I think he deserves some brownie points for that Chris.'

'Mmm. I suppose so. I've given it all a lot of thought and maybe he was just getting sick of us English expecting everyone to speak our language. Anyhow, it's all history. I'm sure we'll enjoy the contents of the box over the next few days.'

It's later in the evening just before dinner, Manfred sound asleep in his basket, that Rob appears with an open bottle of *Gewürztraminer*. It's always been one of my favourite German wines so I'm eager to try it. I watch as Rob pours us each a glass and hands one to me. I'm just about to take the glass to my lips when he coughs loudly in disapproval.

'Really Frau Baird!' he scoffs. 'You wouldn't go down well with the natives supping your wine before everyone has made a toast.'

'*Es tut mir leid!*' I say apologetically.

'Now, look me in the eye,' Rob instructs me.

'What on earth for?' I ask.

'Because not making eye contact before the toast is a good as breaking a mirror, it's incredibly bad luck.'

'Crikey, you have been doing your homework,' I laugh.

'Right, now, we have to say cheers,' he smiles, looking me in the eye.

And so with a cry of '*Prost!*' we raise our glasses. All is well with the world.

BIRDS OF A FEATHER

'THAT'S INTERESTING,' I REMARK looking at a message on the house-sitting website.

'What is?' asks Rob heading for the coffee machine and pouring us both a cup.

'There's someone in Bath asking if we'd be interested in doing a house-sit. They must have found our profile on the website.'

'Well Bath's a lovely city so that's a good start. I can't remember the last time I was there. Who is it and what is it?'

'From what I can gather it's a retired gentleman who has a parrot.'

'A parrot? Good grief, I don't know the first thing about parrots. Is there much information?'

'Not a lot but we could have a video chat with him first if you're interested.'

'So whereabouts in Bath?'

'The Royal Crescent.'

'Now you're talking,' says Rob pulling up a chair next to me so that he can see the screen of the iPad. 'I mean that's pretty exclusive. You couldn't ask for a more upmarket address than that.'

'Let's see what it says in the details. "A third floor apartment in Bath's most prestigious Royal Crescent overlooking the green. This well-appointed property is within easy walking distance of all amenities and the elegant city centre. Polly," ha! That's original, "Polly is an eighteen year-old African grey parrot. She's quite a character and will no doubt keep you amused during your stay. She's easy to care for and has no health issues but sitters will need to keep a watchful eye on her when she's out of her cage." Well that sounds fairly straight forward. What do you reckon?'

'I'm just wondering whether we should be reading into some of those details,' muses Rob. 'We've been caught out before with people's wording. They try to play down any issues and then you find you've taken on a challenge.'

'I know what you mean but what could a parrot get up to? It's hardly going to attack you or trash the place now is it? I'm up for it if you are.'

'Well okay, but I think that we should arrange a video call before we accept.'

'Fine, I'll drop him a line and see if we can arrange something.'

It's the following Sunday evening that we get a video call from Peter, a rather handsome, well-spoken, retired member of the Admiralty Board who looks every inch the sea-captain. His piercing blue eyes and grey hair enhance what appears to be a recently acquired sun-tan. He appears to be in his sitting-room and behind him we can make out a rather magnificent collection of prints depicting sailing-ships against a back-drop of regency-striped wallpaper. Although the signal isn't too good we manage to have a nice chat and discover a little more about the required duties.

'She's easy to care for,' says Peter, taking a drink from a cut-glass tumbler, 'but she has to be watched or she gets up to all sorts of mischief.'

'So do you let her out of her cage all the time?' asks Rob.

'Only when I'm here obviously or she'd wreck the place. She likes attention and if you leave her for any length of time she starts finding ways of attracting you.'

'And do you restrict her to certain rooms?' I ask, beginning to think this might be a little more involved than we'd first imagined.

'Gosh yes, I don't let her into the dining-room, or the bedrooms. So really she's confined to my study where her cage is, the hallway, this lounge and the kitchen, but whatever you do don't leave her in the kitchen unattended or she'll be into everything.'

'And what about her food?' asks Rob.

'She has a special mix which is in a big bag in the pantry and various fruit and veg. I'll leave you some fresh stuff for her and a list of what she can have. And if you wouldn't mind getting some in for her during the second week? I'll leave you some cash, don't worry.'

'And if we needed a vet for any reason?' I ask, always anxious to know that there's an emergency contact.

'I'll leave all that in the book of words but it's only a short walk from here. If you hang on a minute I'll go and get her and you can say hello,' and at that he disappears from view.

I take the opportunity to ask Rob what he thinks about it all. 'I reckon we'd be okay,' he whispers, 'It could be fun and at least we don't have to go for walks in the pouring rain at bedtime. We'd have plenty of time to get out and explore the city too. I'd say yes.'

There's a loud squawking noise as Peter returns with Polly sitting on his hand. She's much bigger than I'd anticipated but quite a pretty bird. Her feathers are a beautiful, soft grey and her tail a startling red.

'Say hello to our new friends,' instructs Peter, as Polly climbs gradually up his arm looking curiously at the screen of the computer, her head tilted to one side. 'Say hello,' he repeats.

'Hello darlin',' comes a rather strangled voice.

'Hello!' we both reply as she stretches her neck forward towards the screen and begins to tap it with her beak. I can't believe I'm talking to a parrot.

'Does she have a very big vocabulary?' asks Rob.

'I'm afraid so and not all of it savoury I'm afraid, so you'll have to excuse the occasional profanity. She came with quite a few phrases and unfortunately I haven't been able to stop her repeating them.'

'So how did she come your way as I assume she's had a previous owner?' I ask.

'She belonged to my late Aunt Maud who bequeathed her to me in her will for my sins,' he laughs, stroking Polly's neck. 'I don't know quite what I did to deserve it. She was twelve when I got her and she's eighteen now but chances are she'll outlive me.'

'Really?' asks Rob in surprise. 'How long do they live?'

'Oh an average of sixty years. Some go on to eighty so, as you can appreciate, I'll be long gone by then.'

'Eighty?' I say, somewhat surprised. 'My goodness, that's a good age. So she's just a youngster then?'

'Yes, she's a stroppy teenager aren't you Pol?' he says, looking at her affectionately. She looks back at him and rubs the side of his head gently with her beak, nibbling at the hair by his ear. 'Stop it!' he laughs.

'Stop it Polly!' cries Polly.

'I'm afraid you'll hear that rather a lot,' says Peter.

'And when we let her out, is she going to be easy to catch?' asks Rob, clearly beginning to take our duties seriously.

'She should go back to her cage if you direct her firmly but if she refuses then something tasty like a grape will usually persuade her. So what do you two reckon? Are you up for it?'

'Yes, we'd love to take her on, wouldn't we Chris?' replies Rob, looking at me for approval.

'Absolutely,' I reply, quietly wondering what we're letting ourselves in for. 'I'll get on and make the travel arrangements and we'll give you a shout in a few days to arrange the hand-over.'

'Splendid!' replies Peter. 'We look forward to meeting you soon. Cheers!' he smiles, raising his glass.

'Bye darlin',' squawks Polly.

It's three weeks later that we find ourselves standing on the doorstep at the Royal Crescent. It's late afternoon but there are still plenty of tourists walking up and down outside admiring the architecture. I press the doorbell on the shiny brass plate next to our host's name and the front door clicks and opens. We step inside into a large, open stairwell with a stone staircase leading elegantly up to the top floor. There are several doors opening off the landings but we continue our climb until we reach Peter's apartment where the door is already open. Rob knocks and a cheery voice from within bids us enter.

'Greetings!' calls Peter, coming hurriedly through from another room. 'You found us! Do come in and here, let me pop your coats in the cloakroom,' he says, helping me off with my jacket. 'I'm so glad you made it. Do go through to the lounge and have a seat. Can I get you a drink either of you? Tea? Coffee? Something stronger?'

I give Rob a look which he knows how to interpret. 'A coffee would be lovely thanks Peter,' he replies.

'Yes, and for me please,' I reply, taking a seat in one of the armchairs. It's a beautiful space, elegantly furnished with pieces befitting the period. The huge, sash windows let plenty of light into the room and a vast, ornate mirror above the stone fireplace has the effect of making the room seem even bigger. A pair of stunning pink and black urn-shaped vases sit at either end of the mantlepiece and in the centre is a magnificent clock in gilt and white marble, each end decorated by a seated female figurine reading a book. It's glorious. I'm still looking around the room taking in our new home when Peter returns with a tray of coffee cups and places it on an imposing, antique coffee table.

'I'm just admiring your clock Peter,' I remark as he kindly hands me my coffee.

'Oh that, yes, another gift from Aunt Maud. I did well there. At least it doesn't cause me any grief! The eagle finial makes it early nineteenth century. I love it too,' he smiles. 'Now you two, as you know I'm leaving shortly, so is there anything else you need to know before I go?'

'Yes, where's Polly?' asks Rob.

'Oh crikey! I haven't even introduced you. I'll tell you what. Have your coffee while I put the last of my things in my bag and then you can meet Polly. I'll show you your room, oh and the central heating, it can get a bit cold in here what with the high ceilings and the big windows.'

A few minutes later we're lead through the hallway and into the study where Polly is sitting in her cage eating a piece of carrot. It's a beautiful cage with ample room for her to move around and decorated with a colourful rope swing and a string of toys for her to play with.

'Here she is the girl,' he says. 'I won't get her out before I go but no doubt she'll want to join you once I've gone. Now you behave for Rob and Christine,' he says softly, stroking her head through the bars. 'I don't want news of any shenanigans while I'm away. You know I'm going, don't you,' he laughs. 'I do hope she'll be alright but feel free to give me a ring if there are any problems. Come and let me show you to your room.'

Although Peter, tries to leave quietly, he receives a noisy send-off from Polly who flaps and squawks and shouts when she hears the door close and starts screaming, 'Bye darlin'. Don't be long!' much to our amusement.

'Well, here we are Mrs Baird, residing in the Royal Crescent no less. I think I'll go and unpack my things if you don't mind or they'll be getting creased,' says Rob heading off to the bedroom.

'Fine. I'll explore the kitchen and try to make sense of the oven and then maybe we should let Polly out?'

'Good idea. I won't be long,' he calls back.

The kitchen is quite out of character with the rest of the house having clearly been totally renovated into an all-singing-all-dancing collection of gadgets and state-of-the-arts machinery. I wander round enviously running my hand over the smooth, granite worktops. There's a spacious walk-in pantry with a good store of all the basics as well as some rather classy-looking jars and tins containing all manner of special goodies. It's just as I'm seeking out the cutlery drawer that an almighty clang reverberates from the hallway. Thinking that Rob must have dropped something I head in the direction of the bedroom only to be met with another very loud, metallic noise which, I realise, is coming from the study. I open the door to find Polly stepping sideways along her perch with her food bowl in her beak and banging it against the bars of her cage.

'Are you trying to tell me something Polly?' I laugh, approaching her gradually so as not to worry her. 'Is it tea-time?'

She responds by dropping the metal bowl on the floor of the cage with a loud clang which brings Rob running down the hallway to investigate.

'Are you alright in here? What on earth's going on?'

'I think our friend's trying to tell us something, aren't you Polly? Maybe she's tired of being cooped up. Do you think we should let her out?'

'Crikey, I must admit I'm a bit nervous Chris. What if we can't get her back in?'

'Well Peter said she could be tempted with a treat. We can't keep her in her cage for our entire stay for heaven's sake.'

'No I suppose you're right but I'm going to let you do the honours, I think I'll just keep out of the way if you don't mind.'

'Okay, but make sure the bedroom doors are closed, and the dining-room,' I call after him.

As Rob goes off to make sure the doors are closed I tentatively release the springs on the door of the cage. Polly's immediately out of the entrance and clambering up onto the roof, eyeing me cautiously. I stand back out of the doorway to give her some space and she's instantly through the door and heading for the kitchen, screaming loudly. I follow her quickly, recalling Peter's warning not to leave her alone in there. I enter slowly and find her strutting along the worktop examining the jars and utensils.

'Hello Polly,' I say quietly. 'What are you up to?'

'Stop it Polly,' she shrieks. I continue to watch her as she jumps onto the rail in front of the range where the t-towels are hanging, latches on to the corner of one with her beak and throws it to the floor with a flourish.

'Now that's naughty,' I say, still keeping my voice calm. As I bend down to pick it up she suddenly leaps from the rail onto my back so that I'm forced to remain doubled over, worried that she might pull the wool of my jumper or, even worse, sink her claws into my flesh.

'Er Polly, I need you to move, come on, jump back on the rail there's a good girl.' However, she remains firmly attached to my sweater until she picks up on Rob's footsteps approaching the kitchen. As he comes through the door she flies off, missing the top of his head by no more than a couple of inches and heads for the sitting-room.

'Good grief!' exclaims Rob. 'That didn't half give me a fright. She just missed the top of my head Chris. I could have been scalped!'

'You came at just the right moment,' I say, stretching back up to my full height. 'Come on, we'd better go and investigate in case she's up to no good.'

We walk quietly into the sitting-room where we find her strutting up and down the mantlepiece in front of the mirror. She stops occasionally and gives her reflection a gentle peck on the glass, cocking her head to one side. We each take a seat at either end of the room and watch her, intrigued to know what she's going to do next. I'm already feeling anxious about the vases and wondering what insurers would make of a claim for breakages by a parrot.

'She seems to be okay with us so far doesn't she? I mean she hasn't got into a flap or anything,' I remark, beginning to relax. 'I'm not so sure about having her on my hand though. I don't much like those scaly feet and those claws look as though they could do you a bit of damage.'

'And her beak I should imagine,' says Rob, watching her every movement carefully from his armchair. 'I remember my grandmother having a budgie when I was small. He used to sit on the top of a picture-frame and peck at the wall-paper until there was a hole there. Then Gran would have to hang another picture to cover up the hole. It used to go on for months until there were so many pictures on the wall she had to wallpaper the room again. The problem was that, for some reason, they never stripped the old wallpaper off before sticking the new stuff up so the walls became springy and lumpy and the room became gradually smaller.'

'Apparently my great-great uncle Edwin used to have a parrot,' I laugh. 'He had a shop that sold fish and game, you remember when the shops used to hang the pheasants and rabbits outside from a rail? Well the story goes that the parrot lived in its cage in the shop.'

'That doesn't sound very hygienic. They wouldn't have got away with it in this day and age that's for sure.'

'No, precisely, but apparently, if my uncle wasn't in the shop and a customer came in the parrot used to call, "Shop you bugger!" He was famous throughout the town.'

'I bet he was. I trust your ancestor didn't have many genteel customers,' laughs Rob.

My story is interrupted as Polly makes a sudden launch and glides over onto the arm of my chair, causing us both to jump.

'Crikey, I wasn't expecting that,' I say nervously. 'Hello Polly. Have you come to see me?'

I sit absolutely still, quietly panicking about what she's likely to do next. To my horror she steps from the arm of the chair onto my arm and begins to climb gradually up to my shoulder. I look in Rob's direction, my face screwed up in alarm. She suddenly spies my earring and decides to peck at it, making it swing from my ear.

'No Polly. I don't like that,' I say firmly but quietly.

'Stop it Polly,' she squawks in my ear.

'I'll tell you what, let's go back to the kitchen and see if we can find you something nice to eat, shall we?' and with that I stand up very slowly and begin to walk back to the kitchen, Polly happily balanced on my shoulder. I'm anticipating her flying off at any moment but she stays put until we reach the kitchen door where she makes a short flight to the back of one of the chairs. I'm hugely relieved and head for the pantry to find something tempting for her. There's a huge bowl full of all manner of exotic fruit so I break off a small bunch of grapes and take them over to where she's sitting.

'What have I got?' I ask, holding out my hand to show her the fruit.

'Grape!' she replies, much to my surprise.

'Yes, good girl, it is a grape. Here you are,' I say holding one out in her direction. Still balanced on the back of the chair she reaches forward and gently takes it from my hand. 'Good girl!' I say animatedly, hoping that she'll pick up on the fact that I'm pleased with her. 'Come on then, let's go back to your cage and you can have some more grapes,' I say walking slowly in the direction of the study and hoping that she's going to follow me. To my relief she soars past me into the study where she lands on the roof of the cage.

'Grape!' she squawks excitedly, 'grape! Grape!'

'Yes, you can have your grapes but you have to go in your cage. Come on,' I say coaxingly, and drop the remaining fruit into her bowl. To my relief she makes her way down the front of the cage and steps through the door onto her perch. I waste no time in closing the door firmly behind her, checking that the latches are firmly in place. She's already got her head in her bowl and seems quite happy to be back inside. I can feel myself physically relax and head back to the sitting-room to report my success.

'Mission accomplished!' I announce triumphantly.

'Oh well done sweetheart, what a relief. I was dreading us having to chase her around flinging sheets over her head. I reckon you deserve a glass don't you?'

We wake early the next morning with the sun streaming through the window onto the bed. The sky is a startling blue and it promises to be a beautiful day.

'Let's get up and make the most of it shall we?' suggests Rob. 'It would be a shame not to get out and explore,' he says, wandering over to the window to admire the view. It really is splendid as we can look out over the extensive lawned area to the front of the property or sideways along the graceful curve of the crescent, the elegant row of houses being one of the most celebrated architectural attractions of the city, the mellow Bath stone glowing warm in the morning sun. There are already people with cameras and mobile phones walking along the pavement below taking photos.

'It really is magnificent isn't it?' I sigh. 'I can just imagine it in Jane Austen's time with the ladies walking up and down with their parasols hoping to catch sight of the militia. It must have been so romantic. Anyhow, I suppose I'd better go and attend to Polly or she'll start protesting.' I wander through to the study and remove the cloth that is draped over the top of her cage.

'Morning darlin',' she says, climbing up the side of her cage and pecking at one of her toys.

'Oh, good morning Polly,' I reply, somewhat amused by her greeting. 'I'll come back soon and get your breakfast. Won't be long.'

'Have a nice day,' she squawks as I go back to the bedroom where Rob is still standing at the window.

'Speaking of the militia, come and take a look over here,' he says, pointing down to the pavement below. 'It seems that you're in luck. Either my eyes are deceiving me or the militia's in town.'

I join him at the window and, sure enough, on the pavement below a group of young men in handsome red jackets and white trousers is gathering. They're in full uniform, their tall black hats displaying the gold insignia of King George. They really do look rather splendid.

'Good grief, they've even got guns! I wonder what's going on?'

'Maybe they're a tourist attraction or something?' suggests Rob. 'Places like Bath often have people dressed up in costume to attract the crowds.'

'Mmm, but they're starting a bit early aren't they? It's only eight o'clock. Anyhow, I'm going to go and have a shower and then we can think about some breakfast.'

'That would be good. I'll make the bed, just give me a shout when you're out.'

I've only been in the shower a matter of minutes when the telephone starts ringing. 'Rob,' I shout, 'telephone!'

His head appears round the bathroom door. 'Sorry darling did you call?'

'Yes, the telephone's ringing, can you go and answer it?'

'Yes of course, but where is it?'

'How on earth am I supposed to know? Just follow the sound.'

He heads off but comes back almost immediately.

'It was coming from the study but the minute I got there it stopped.'

'Oh well, I'm sure whoever it was could leave a message. It can't have been Peter, he'd have used my mobile. Never mind. They can always ring back.'

It's while we're tucking in to breakfast in the kitchen that the phone rings again.

'I'll get it, stay where you are,' I say, getting up and heading for the study.

As I approach the door I can hear Polly clattering about and, when I open the door I find her pulling at the door of her cage and emitting a loud ring-tone.

'So it's you!' I laugh. 'It wasn't a real telephone at all. Is this your way of getting some attention Polly-wolly-doodle? Do you want some breakfast, is that what it is?'

'Stop it Polly!' she cackles.

'Yes, you'd better stop it you horror,' I smile heading back to the kitchen to get her food.

'So who was it?' asks Rob, pouring another cup of coffee.

'Polly,' I reply.

'Polly? What do you mean?'

'It wasn't a real telephone, it was Polly pretending to be a telephone,' I laugh. 'Isn't that amazing?'

'I'd never have believed it. Seriously?'

'Yes, seriously. It's obviously a trick she's learnt in order to get a response.'

'Well I never. I wouldn't have thought it possible. It sounded so realistic.'

'I'm just going to feed her and then maybe we can get out and enjoy the sunshine? We can let her out when we get back.'

We wander along the Crescent and onto the Circus, an equally elegant, grand architectural delight of the city. It's just as we turn the corner that we narrowly avoid bumping into a rather well-dressed gentleman sporting a frock-coat and cravat with a young lady on each arm, both of whom are dressed in regency costume and carrying parasols, their bonnets tied neatly under their chins with a large bow.

'I do beg your pardon Mr Bennett!' I laugh and, as the gentleman doffs his hat, the girls giggle before proceeding in the direction from which we've just come.

'Well this is very jolly,' remarks Rob turning and watching them walk towards the Crescent. 'I wonder if people like to dress up just for the fun of it when they come here?'

'Well there are thousands of Jane Austen devotees so maybe they do, but it does add to the feel of the place. I'd love to have done that when I was younger.'

'And you would have looked most ravishing if I may say so Mrs Baird,' says Rob, bowing and taking me by the arm.

We spend a good hour exploring the immediate area before calling into the local supermarket for some urgent supplies. Rob wanders off to find some wine but comes hurrying back.

'Darling, you may not believe this but I've just seen a gentleman dressed as an admiral rummaging around in the freezers. You don't suppose there's something going on do you? I mean surely the place isn't normally riddled with people in costume?'

'Maybe they're making a film?' I suggest. 'It's the ideal place for anything set in the regency period. They've got the perfect backdrop in the Crescent or the Circus. Anyhow, if we've got everything we'd better not linger, we need to get back and let Polly out.'

It's on turning into the Crescent that we are greeted not only by soldiers of the militia, but ladies, young and old, wearing long dresses and bonnets, elderly gentlemen with side-whiskers in frock-coats, a parson, a town-crier, men in tricorne and stove-pipe hats, dashing young men sporting smart cravats, it's like walking into one of Austen's novels.

'Oh how wonderful!' I exclaim. 'Oh isn't it fabulous? What a treat! But as you say, there must be something going on. There must be a couple of hundred people here.'

At that moment an elderly gentleman in uniform walks up to us, salutes, hands us a leaflet then bows courteously before walking on to a group of Japanese tourists.

'So what does it say?' I ask.

'It seems to be a programme of sorts. Yes, it's the Jane Austen Festival. "Ten days of events, lectures, walks, dances and more".

We'll have to have a closer look when we get home and, speaking of which, we'd better make a move and let poor Polly out before she has a moody.'

In spite of our absence Polly seems to be in good humour and, on having her cage door opened, glides through to the kitchen where she perches on the top of the door so that she can watch our every move.

'Hello Polly,' I call up to her but she ignores me, turning herself round so that all I can see is her back. 'Oh, aren't you speaking to me today?'

'I reckon she's in a huff because we went out and left her,' says Rob, settling on one of the chairs and looking up at her. 'She seemed to be getting on alright with you yesterday but she hasn't shown any interest in me at all.'

'I reckon that that's because you're a man and she prefers women. They say that African greys tend to bond with one person. Why don't you feed her today? It might put you in her good books.'

'Okay, I'll give it a go. It's a cupful of the mix and some fruit isn't it?'

'Yes, or some veg. There's plenty in the pantry.'

Polly immediately turns round at the sound of the pantry door opening and waits for Rob to emerge. As he heads for the study with her food she launches herself off the door and heads for her cage. I can hear a lot of flapping and banging and then suddenly a loud squawk.

'Well, so much for making friends. I've just been bitten,' he complains, sucking at his finger. 'And that beak of hers is blooming sharp I can tell you. Look!' he says, holding out his finger to show me the wound.

'Oh Rob, it's only a peck. It's gone a bit red that's all. You won't die.'

'I might! Don't parrots carry that disease, what's it called,

198

pneumoconiosis?'

'You mean psittacosis. Yes, but it's extremely rare and you won't know for at least a few days if you've got it. You'll be fine. If you develop a fever we'll get you to the infectious disease department of the hospital and put you in quarantine for a few weeks.'

'That isn't terribly funny Chris. And in future you can feed her. I'm not going to risk any further injury thank you very much.' And having said that he picks up his book from the kitchen table and heads off to the sitting-room.

Having finished cleaning up I wander through to see what he's up to only to find him watching the television. Having given up having a tele years ago it's always a bit of a novelty to have access to one.

'What are you watching darling?' I ask, settling down on the sofa next to him.

'It's a National Geographic programme about the islands in the Pacific.'

'That sounds interesting.'

'It is, there's some stunning scenery, real desert island stuff,' he says examining his finger and sucking it again. 'I guess that's where parrots go on holiday,' he smirks.

'What do you mean?'

'Polynesia!' he laughs.

'Oh very funny,' I say, giving him a quick dig in the ribs with my elbow.

There's a sudden commotion as, with an almighty display of flapping and squawking, Polly appears and lands on the back of the sofa.

'Are you protesting at Uncle Rob's terrible joke Polly?' I ask, turning to watch her sidling towards us.

'Where do parrots go for their further education?' laughs Rob.

'Oh no, please don't start. I have no idea.'

'To a polytechnic!'

There's a sudden loud shriek and a strangled cry that sounds horribly like 'shut up you fat bastard' and, before Rob has had a chance to laugh out loud at his own joke, Polly has made her way along the back of the sofa, bent forward and taken a good nip at his ear. He leaps up off the sofa clearly shaken.

'She attacked me!' he cries, covering his ear with his hand and walking over to the mirror to examine the damage. 'This is getting beyond a joke Chris. Not only is this bird physically aggressive she's foul-mouthed too. You'll have to put her back in her cage. There's no way I'm going to sit here and be assaulted. That's twice now.'

I try hard not to let him see that I'm finding it all slightly amusing but my expression is a giveaway.

'I'm being serious Chris. No way am I going to sit in the same room as that avian beast. I'm going to the bedroom, I'll leave it to you to put her in her cage. I'm going to tend to my wounds and perhaps you'd be good enough to let me know when I can safely reemerge.' And with that he flounces off down the passage to the bedroom, his hand clasped firmly over his ear.

'Oh dear Polly. You're not very popular. Poor Uncle Rob,' I laugh as she shuffles sideways along the back of the settee. To my alarm with a sudden leap she lands on my head. 'Er, Polly, I'm not so sure I like this,' I say quietly as she starts pulling at strands of my hair, albeit gently. 'No Polly,' I say more sternly as she yanks at another strand.

'Stop it Polly,' she squawks. But she doesn't. She's clearly enjoying herself, tugging at another wisp of my hair.

'That's enough thank you, I think it's time you went back in your cage.'

She's clearly picked up on my intention and with one short flight is over to the window and climbing up the curtain. I realise that I'm too nervous to touch her and I'm still a bit twitchy about having her scaly claws wrapped round my hand. I decide that the best tactic is to go and find something tasty and tempt her back into her cage so I head for the kitchen and the pantry. No sooner am I through the door than a loud flapping tells me that she's followed me but I choose to ignore her.

'I want to go back now,' comes her strangled voice from behind me. I'm quite taken aback by her announcement.

'Well you can go back Polly and here, I've got a nice piece of melon for you. Come on, let's go back to your cage.'

She pops back into her cage quite happily and starts tucking into her melon, grasping it with one foot and tearing off pieces with her beak. I check that she's got plenty of water and then head off to the bedroom to rescue Rob.

'You can come out now Van Gogh, the coast's clear,' I call through the door. Rob sticks his head out and looks suspiciously down the hallway. 'It's alright, she's in her cage so you needn't worry.'

'Have you looked in the mirror recently?' he asks having examined my head. 'You look like the wild man of Borneo.'

I wander back to the sitting-room and take a look at myself in the mirror. Rob's right. Polly has made a good job of re-styling my hair into something akin to a vagrant.

'That's Polly's doing,' I laugh. 'She decided to sit on my head and play with my hair. I'd better go and give it a brush.'

As I head towards the bathroom I suddenly realise that all the lights in the study are on. I don't recall switching them on but maybe I did without thinking. I stick my hand round the door, switch the lights off at the wall and go into the bathroom to sort my hair out. It really is a tangled mess and takes some time to rearrange. Having combed it through I head back to the sitting-room but to my puzzlement the lights are on again in the study.

'Rob,' I call. 'Have you by any chance just put the lights on in the study?'

'No, not guilty,' comes the reply. 'There's no way I'm going anywhere near that cannibal, even if she is in a cage.'

'Well that's odd. I thought I'd just switched them off but they're back on again.'

'You probably just forgot. It's what happens when you get old,' he sniggers.

'Less of the old Mr Baird,' I call back. 'Anyhow, I'll leave them on now so that Polly has a bit of light.' She's playing with some of her toys and hanging upside down on the rope swing that is suspended from the top of her cage. 'If you don't mind darling I'd like to go down and take some photos of the people in costume. It's such a wonderful backdrop. Do you want to come?'

'No, I'll stay here and read my book if you don't mind. I wouldn't want to cramp your style with all those dashing young men. Just don't go eloping with one of those handsome soldiers. I'll be keeping an eye on you from up here.'

It really is the most wonderful photo-opportunity. The participants have obviously gone to great lengths to ensure that their costumes are authentic and I spend a good half hour wandering around capturing the mood of the day. Everyone is in good humour and there is much laughing and jollity. Both young and old Austen devotees are clearly in their element. It's a photographer's dream but, needless to say, my camera battery runs out just when I most need it so I head reluctantly back to the apartment.

'Hello darling, did you have a productive time?' asks Rob.

'Yes thanks until my battery went flat. What about you?'

'I'm fine thanks but I think there must be a problem with the lights in the study. They've been going on and off sporadically ever since you left. I think we might need to call an electrician. There must be a faulty switch or circuit or something.'

'Well we'd need to speak to Peter about it before calling anyone. He might use a particular electrician too. I've got his number on my phone. If you don't mind ringing him I'll put the kettle on and make us a cup of tea.'

'Alright Polly,' he replies. 'Let me have the number and I'll give him a call now.'

'Ha ha. Here you are, you can use my phone.'

I wander into the kitchen to make the tea and can just catch snippets of the conversation.

'No, they seem to be going on and off of their own accord … yes, that's right … what? … really? … good grief, whoever would have believed it? … yes, I'm sure you're right … I'll go and check, but no doubt that's what's happening but I'm absolutely astonished. Alright then Peter, have a good evening. Goodbye.'

'So what was all that about? Is he happy about us getting somebody in?'

'It seems it won't be necessary but you're never going to believe this.'

'What?'

'Peter says it's one of Polly's tricks.'

'Polly? How on earth can she switch the lights on and off, she's in her cage for goodness sake,' I say disbelievingly.

'She talks to Alexa!'

'Sorry?' I gasp, hardly believing what I'm hearing.

'She tells Alexa to put the lights on and off. Apparently she has other tricks too like telling her to shut up or asking for facts.'

'No! That's amazing! I hadn't even noticed that Peter had Alexa in there.'

'Nor had I or I'd have switched her off myself,' replies Rob who has always been convinced that Alexa is listening in to our conversations and recording them. 'Let's go and investigate.'

We creep quietly along to the study where our feathered friend is hanging upside down.

'Hello darlin',' she squawks.

'Hello Polly,' I say, putting my finger through the bars of her cage and stroking her head. 'Have you been talking to Alexa?' She immediately turns her head away from me. 'What have you been saying?' There's no reply and Polly shuffles along her perch, jumps down onto the floor of her cage and starts flinging her bowl around.

'Maybe we'll just have to listen in later and see if we can catch her at it?' I suggest.

'It seems like it. I wish I'd realised that Peter had got Alexa in here. I find it very disconcerting.'

'I really don't understand why darling. It isn't as though you work for MI5 or something.'

'Yes, but Peter worked for the Admiralty. They might be spying on him for all we know.'

'Well it seems that they'd end up talking to a parrot so I wouldn't get too upset about it.'

It's early in the evening while we're relaxing in the sitting-room that we hear a faint voice and, lo and behold, the lights go on in the study. I beckon to Rob and we quietly sneak towards the door.

'Alexa, all lights off!' commands Polly and, sure enough, the room is plunged into darkness. 'Alexa, all lights on!' she squawks again.

We look at each other in amazement, trying to stifle our laughter but end up having a fit of the giggles as the light floods into the hallway from the study.

'Hello darlin', comes the voice from behind the door. 'Stop it Polly! Alexa shut up! Stop it Polly! Have a nice day!'

'I think she's trying out her repertoire,' I laugh, 'but it's amazing what she comes out with isn't it?'

'I never for a moment dreamt that a parrot would talk to Alexa. Maybe she finds her good company when she's on her own?'

'Well I suppose birds get lonely in the same way that we do. Anyhow, what about some food? I'd better get on with dinner or it'll be supper time soon. Hopefully it won't take long. If I get it started could you keep an eye on things if I go and have a shower?'

'Of course. Just give me a shout.'

It's a joy to have such a well-equipped kitchen and after a quick rummage in the cupboards for a few spices I manage to knock together a curry of sorts. Leaving the pan on a low heat I give Rob a shout and tell him I'm off to have my shower. There's a faint reply from the sitting-room so I head off to the bathroom to freshen up.

The bathroom is huge with an original slipper-bath and a loo with an overhead cistern and pull-chain. It puts me in mind of my grandparents' outdoor lavatory where the toilet-paper was made up of torn up sheets of newspaper stuck on a nail that was driven into the wall. There was a always a strong smell of damp and distemper in there as it had to be redecorated on a regular basis. I recall my grandfather heading outside with his flat cap on and a newspaper under his arm and disappearing for what seemed to be an inordinate length of time. I smile at the memories and step into the shower. It occurs to me that maybe it would be a good idea to wash my hair while I'm in there having had a parrot walking about on my head. Having just massaged the shampoo into my hair I'm suddenly aware of a loud noise akin to a siren coming from along the corridor. Somewhat anxious I quickly turn off the water, grab a towel and drip my way long the hallway to find Rob in the kitchen removing a smouldering pan of acrid remains from the hob.

'What on earth? Oh Rob, you didn't forget about the pan?' I snap. 'You know I asked you to keep an eye on it,' I moan, fanning the air with my hand to disperse the blue smoke.

'I know darling, I'm so sorry,' coughs Rob, choking on the fumes. 'I must have dozed off. Fortunately Polly raised the alarm.'

'Polly? How did she manage that?'

'She did her best impression of a smoke-detector and it

woke me up so we've got her to thank or this could have been a lot more serious. I'm so sorry. But it's quite incredible isn't it, that she was able to raise the alarm?' he splutters as more smoke enters his lungs.

'Absolutely and thank goodness she did, the whole place could have gone up in flames. We'd better get the extractor fan on and open a couple of windows. The smell in here's dreadful and it'll permeate the place if we don't do something quickly. I reckon Polly deserves a treat for saving the day!'

It's later in the evening when the phone rings. It's Peter calling from his hotel to make sure we're okay. I'm reluctant to let him know that we narrowly escaped burning the place down but I'm also intrigued to know how Polly was able to react. I play down the extent of the culinary disaster but explain how she managed to alert us to the smell of burning.

'Well that's amazing!' says Peter. 'We used to have a smoke detector at the last place that used to go off at regular intervals whenever I burnt the toast. She must have started to associate the noise with the smell. Clever girl eh?'

'Absolutely, we could have had a nasty accident, that's for sure. Anyhow, please don't worry, I assure you everything's okay. Enjoy the rest of your stay and thanks for calling.'

Having had to cook an alternative meal for dinner after our little disaster it's rather late by the time we head for bed. In spite of us having opened windows in every room the smell of burnt curry has now taken hold of the whole apartment. Having ensured that all the windows have been closed I go into the study to put Polly to bed for the night.

'Well Polly, you saved the day didn't you?' She cocks her head on one side as if to show that she's listening and I wonder just how much she actually understands. I realise that I've vastly underestimated her ability and that there's clearly evidence of two-way communication, not just her having learnt stock phrases 'parrot fashion'. 'Here, I've brought you a carrot,' I say, passing it to her through the bars of the cage. 'You were a clever girl weren't you?' She takes the carrot in her beak and then pins it to her perch with her foot. 'Night night then sweetheart,' I whisper as I lay her blanket over the cage.

'Night darlin', comes the reply.

By the time I climb into bed Rob is already drifting off to sleep. He's obviously sensed me slipping into bed beside him and mumbles a quiet, 'Goodnight darling,' before pulling the covers up over his head.

''Night you fat bastard,' I giggle, 'sleep tight.'

A LITTLE EGGCITEMENT

'I KNOW YOU'VE ALREADY told me but remind me, where are we off to this time?' asks Rob, removing his glasses and looking quizzically at me. 'I don't want any excitement, just a change of scenery and a furry friend or two.'

'A lovely timber-framed cottage in a Herefordshire village, but I'm afraid your friends will have feathers not fur.'

'Oh. What sort of feathers? I hope we're not talking more parrots?'

'Nope. Chickens.'

'Chickens? That'll be a first for us. But isn't that going to be a bit dull? I mean you can't exactly have a relationship with a chicken, can you?'

'I don't know. I've seen videos of people hugging chickens so maybe they are affectionate but just don't get the opportunity to show it. Most of the time they're kept enclosed so you wouldn't normally interact with them, but this lot are free range. Apparently the family have a dog too but she's going with them.'

'Oh. That's a pity. I like to have a dog around the place.'

'Never mind. It'll give us the freedom to get out and about. It's a beautiful part of the country. There's some wonderful scenery and you'll be happy to learn that it's cider country.'

'So when do we start?' asks Rob eagerly, his face lighting up at the mention of the word cider.

'A week on Saturday but we'll need to book the ferry and allow plenty of time to get there. It's quite a drive. So go on, get packing! You've only got ten days to organise your wardrobe.'

The Herefordshire landscape is quite spectacular with rolling hills and huge tracts of open countryside. Our route takes us on blissfully quiet roads through several villages on the 'black and white trail' where the houses are timber-framed but where, over the years, they have had their timbers painted black with bitumen to protect them. It's a beautiful area and makes me realise how we lack woodland on our island, the salt air restricting the variety of trees that grow there. Many of the surrounding fields are apple orchards full of trees in blossom; there's a chocolate-box image in every direction.

'The country-side's really beautiful here isn't it? And it's such a joy to be able to drive on quiet roads,' muses Rob. 'None of that sitting bumper to bumper in a traffic jam.'

'Yes, it is a joy, isn't it? Oh, hang on, I think this is us coming up on the right darling,' I interrupt, pointing to an open five-bar gate. As Rob turns the car into the drive a loud barking can be heard from the cottage. 'I'm assuming this is the right place. Yes, this is it,' I say, noticing the name of the house on the wall. '"Honeysuckle Cottage". How lovely.'

Before we've managed to get out of the car a handsome spaniel has come to check us out, her tail wagging furiously and her nose investigating the pair of us.

'Hello,' says Rob, 'you're a lovely lady.'

'And she's a terrible flirt!' comes a voice from the porch. 'Hi, I'm David, you must be Chris and Rob. Lovely to meet you at last,' he says, walking over to shake hands. 'That's Molly, our wonder dog. I'll tell you all about her later. Anyhow, do come in and meet the family. Have you had a good journey?'

'Yes thanks,' replies Rob following him into the house. 'This neck of the woods is a delight after the roads further south, it's so wonderfully quiet.'

'Yes, apart from at harvest time when we get stuck behind tractors,' he laughs. 'This is my wife Susan,' he says as a young woman, probably in her mid thirties, appears from the back of the house. She has the air of a hippy about her with a long flowing skirt and a wrist adorned by numerous bracelets that make a pretty noise as she reaches out her hand to greet us.

'Hello. So you found us!' she smiles, brushing back her long red hair with her hand.

'Yes, no trouble at all thanks,' replies Rob. 'Fortunately I have a good navigator,' he says, smiling at me.

'Well do come and have a seat in the conservatory,' invites David. 'You can enjoy the scenery more and the farmer's just put the lambs in the field so you'll have some entertainment as well.'

He's a tall, slim man but difficult to age. I reckon he probably looks a little older than he is as his clothing is a bit dated; cords, brogues and a plain white shirt with a cravat at the neck. I can't recall the last time I saw a man in a cravat but decide it's rather fetching.

'Matthew,' he calls. 'Come and say hello to our visitors.'

A young boy, probably about fourteen years old, appears from an adjacent room and dutifully greets us as instructed. He looks slightly embarrassed by the attention and glances furtively at his father as if hoping to be given permission to return to whatever he was doing before we arrived.

'Molly is Matthew's dog,' explains David. 'Matt has type 1 diabetes which means he gets no warning if his blood sugar suddenly fluctuates. Molly can detect his sugar levels with her nose and alert him so he can live a fairly normal life.'

'Oh my, that's astounding!' says Rob. 'I've often heard about assistance dogs but didn't realise they could help with conditions like diabetes. You're lucky to have such a wonderful friend,' he says turning to the boy. 'How old is she Matthew?'

Matthew looks for support from his father who gives him an encouraging smile.

'She's four now,' he replies.

'And how long have you had her?' I ask.

There's another furtive glance at David who nods at him reassuringly.

'Two years,' he replies, his eyes returning quickly to the floor.

'She's changed our lives,' says Susan. 'Before Molly came along we had endless emergency call-outs and trips to the hospital as we had no warning that Matthew's sugar-levels were changing. Molly lets Matthew know straight away when he needs his medication.'

'Oh my, that's truly amazing,' says Rob. 'So how does she alert?'

'She'll simply stop what she's doing and sit. Then she'll stare at him until he gets his kit and tests himself. If need be she'll actually go and get his kit for him,' replies David. 'If they're out walking she'll just stop and refuse to move until he tests his blood sugar.'

'You mean she actually delivers the kit to wherever he is?' asks Rob in astonishment.

'Yes,' replies Susan. 'Amazing isn't it?' she says looking fondly at her son. 'Go on, you can go back to your room,' she laughs. 'I can see we're embarrassing you. Go and make sure you've got everything because we'll be leaving in a couple of hours.'

Matthew, obviously hugely relieved to be allowed to leave, smiles and disappears up the stairs, closely followed by Molly.

'I can't tell you what a difference she's made to our lives. We were both living on a knife edge when Matt was diagnosed. He could have up to six or eight hypos a day with no warning and just collapse on the spot. We felt we couldn't let him out of our sight and were up half the night checking on him,' says David, the memories still strong by the look on his face. 'Susan used to dread the phone ringing when he was at school because, more often than not, it was to let us know that they'd had to call an ambulance and that he was on his way to the hospital. He spent so many nights there it was horrendous. We were both wrecks.'

'So how did you find out that a dog could help?' asks Rob, clearly fascinated by all we've been told.

'I read an article in a magazine about the work being done by Medical Detection Dogs,' replies Susan, 'and got in touch to see if a dog could in any way help Matthew. They felt there was a strong possibility which was great news. They were wonderful to work with although I have to say it was hard work at first as establishing a bond between Matt and Molly was crucial, but to be honest it seemed as though they were meant for each other. He adores her, doesn't he David?'

'He does. They're absolutely inseparable,' he smiles.

'Well, enough of our lives! You two would probably welcome the chance to freshen up and then I'll make you a cup of tea and show you the chickens,' says Susan, picking herself up from the floor where she's been sitting. 'And I'll give you both a quick guided tour of the house, but it's really very straightforward.'

'Well that's astonishing!' says Rob as we start to unpack our cases. 'I would never have believed it possible. Aren't dogs wonderful?'

'Absolutely, and Molly clearly helps him with his confidence. He's a shy lad.'

'But to be able to detect a change in someone's blood sugar by smell. It really is amazing.'

'Well if you want to get on with your unpacking and arranging your wardrobe I'll go down and find out about the chickens. I'll see you downstairs when you're ready. Oh, and mind your head on the beams, these door frames are rather low,' I call back.

Susan is already waiting for me so we head off down the garden to a large area that's surrounded by chicken wire. Half a dozen chickens are scratching away at the grass and come running towards us as we arrive.

'So these are the girls,' announces Susan. 'They're no trouble at all. Their feed is in here,' she says, lifting the lid off a large galvanised dustbin, 'you'll need three scoops of that each morning and their water needs topping up daily, the tap is just over there,' she says, pointing towards the shed. 'They're generally pretty tidy but I'd appreciate it if you could remove any mess or wet-patches every day and put it in the other bin, it just helps to keep infections at bay. There's plenty of fresh straw in the shed here,' she says, opening the door to show me. 'The biggest worry is the foxes so please make sure you put the chickens to bed before it gets dark. They'll come to the coop quite happily. Oh, and of course, help yourselves to eggs. It's best if you write the date on them as you collect them so that you know which are the freshest.'

'Well that all sounds pretty straight forward. So do you have much of a problem with foxes?' I ask, curious to know as we don't have any at home.

'Sadly yes. They tend to keep away during the day but they'd kill the whole flock if they were left out at night.'

'Crikey! That sounds serious. We tend to forget what it's like to have predators living where we do.'

'So don't you have foxes on the island?' asks Susan, obviously surprised.

'No. Nor badgers, squirrels, toads, moles, hares or snakes. Apart from birds of prey or dogs, chickens are pretty safe.'

'I wish they were here. We lost a whole flock a couple of years ago so we tend to be ultra-careful.'

'We'll be sure to make certain they're tucked up in the evening, don't worry,' I reassure her.

I wake the following morning to sun streaming through the window and warming my face then climb out of bed to admire the view to the back of the house beyond the chicken enclosure. The garden backs onto an apple orchard and beyond it sits the local church with its slender steeple, the golden cockerel on the top glinting in the morning sun. The surrounding fields are dotted with black and white cottages, many of them listing to one side as their frames have buckled and twisted over centuries.

'So who's going to let the chickens out and make the coffee?'

I ask of the sleepy head that's still buried under the covers. A groan suggests that it's me. 'Okay, but you're on breakfast duty Mr Baird. I'm going to grab a shower so I'll see you downstairs when you've managed to crawl out of your scratcher,' I laugh heading for the bathroom.

The chickens are pleased to be given their freedom and come scuttling out into the garden, wings flapping after their night of confinement. I scatter their feed over the ground in the enclosure and then stand back to watch them for a while. One of them looks decidedly scrawny with a half-bare neck and seems intent on preventing any of the rest of the gang from having their breakfast. She mounts an attack on all around her and seems particularly aggressive towards one poor creature who has clearly learned to avoid her bullying beak. A small group of lambs comes skipping over to the back fence bleating loudly, curious but clearly nervous. They bounce along the boundary before rushing back to their mothers to feed. As they reach for their milk with outstretched necks the ewes are butted skyward by their eager offspring. It really is idyllic.

I wander back into the cottage to find Rob sitting at the table which he has laid ready for breakfast. 'Oh well done darling. Thanks for getting everything ready.'

'No problem,' he replies. 'Coffee?'

'Oh that sounds wonderful!' I reply pulling up a chair. It's only then that I notice Rob holding the side of his head. 'Are you alright? Have you got a headache or something?'

'Only since I cracked my head on the beam in the bathroom. I forgot about the lack of headroom above the washbasin and stood up too quickly when I was cleaning my teeth. It's alright it'll go.'

'Poor thing. You'll just have to be careful in future,' I sympathise while tucking into a thick slice of toast and honey. 'Mmm, I could get use to this.'

'What's that? Me making breakfast or us living in the English country-side?'

'Both, particularly breakfast. You make a good cup of coffee Mr Baird. It's just so lovely to feel immersed in the natural world, what with the chickens and the lambs and the fields all around. All I'd need would be a dog or three.'

My hankering after another dog has met with constant dismissal by Rob, especially as my chosen breed would be a Newfoundland. Our discussions over the amount of space needed, the cost of feeding, their short life-span along with the resultant health-issues and heartbreak, not to mention the need to mop up copious amounts of drool, have been an ongoing but fruitless debate for some time. Somehow I fail to impress upon him my need for a huge, huggable, slobbering, bear of a dog.

'So what's the plan for the day?' he asks, topping up my coffee. 'Are we going to explore the village?'

'Absolutely and we'll need to get a few bits and bobs from the store. I think we can get by without a drive to the supermarket and anyhow, it's good to patronise the local shops.'

'Sounds good. And maybe a pub lunch?'

'Oh yes please, that sounds perfect.'

The local pub is the quintessential English hostelry with low beams, horse brasses and a blazing log fire. Our host is a jovial, beefy sort of fellow with an unusually large head and heavy jowls but with a genial smile and a cordial manner.

'Good morning. And what can I be getting for you?' he asks, leaning on the counter.

'I think we'd both like to sample some of the local cider please,' replies Rob, examining the hand pumps.

'Well, we've got Bulmers Strongbow or Woodpecker.'

'I reckon we'll both go for the Strongbow' replies Rob.

'Right, sir. So will that be a half or a pint?'

'Oh I'll manage a pint but I reckon a half for my wife. Is that right Chris?' he asks, turning to me.

'Sounds perfect thanks and do you do a ploughman's lunch by any chance?'

'We do indeed, my dear. Will that be two?'

'It will indeed thank you,' replies Rob.

'Well there's the cider sir, and if you'd like to take a seat the food'll be with you shortly.'

We take ourselves over to a table by the open log fire and settle down in a couple of comfy armchairs.

'Well this is the life darling. There's nothing like a good English pub. I wish we had this sort of thing at home.'

'Yes, I know what you mean. There's a really special feel isn't there, and I just love the smell of wood-smoke. Oh my, it looks as though we've got company!'

A very stocky bulldog has come to say hello. A big beast with a drooling jaw who's very keen to meet Rob.

'Hello boy. My you're a big fellow,' says Rob, reaching down to scratch the dog's head. 'So where have you come from?'

'I'm afraid he's just escaped from our sitting-room,' comes a voice from the doorway as our host enters, carrying a tray. 'Sorry about that, I'll grab him in a moment. There we go, two ploughmans for the lady and gentleman,' he announces, setting the two plates down on the table. 'Here Winston, come out of everyone's way. I'm sorry about that. He's a sociable boy, but he won't hurt you. So are you good people just passing through?'

'No, we're here for a few days actually,' replies Rob. 'We're house-sitting for a family while they're on holiday.'

'Oh, that'll be the Jenkins then. The couple with the lad who has Molly.'

'That's right, you obviously know them,' replies Rob.

'Yes, everyone knows Molly. Amazing animal. She's changed that lad's life, and the family's. It's incredible the way she watches over the boy. She woke us all up to what these dogs can do. We even hold a dog show in the village every year as a fundraiser for the charity. In fact you'll probably still be here for it. It's a week tomorrow.'

'Oh that would be wonderful!' I reply. 'We'll have to make a note in the diary.'

'Anyhow, nice to meet you. I'd better get on or I'll be in trouble with the kitchen. Come on you,' he says, grabbing Winston's collar and leading him back through the door. I can't help but notice his rather bandy legs as he heads back to the kitchen, Winston waddling close behind, his big fat bottom disappearing into the distance.

'That would be nice wouldn't it Rob, a dog show? I can't say I've been to one since Holly won the best veteran,' I say, taking a sip of my cider.

'Crikey, that must be ten years ago Chris. It's hard to believe isn't it?'

The rosette that our dear old lady had won is still hanging on the fridge at home. Sometimes it's hard to let go of the memories.

We wake early again the following morning with the sunrise. It's lovely to lie back and look up at the timbers in the roof, some really twisted with time.

'It's amazing to think that those bits of wood have been here for over three hundred years isn't it?' I muse. 'It makes me wonder about the people who've lived here over the years. Did you notice that one of the floorboards has been repaired with the sole of a shoe?'

'Yes I did. And didn't they sometimes hide a shoe in a wall when they were building as a sort of good luck charm?'

'I think you're right. I wonder what they'd hide there these days?'

'Probably a Nike trainer or worse,' laughs Rob. 'You can't imagine the houses that are being built today still standing in a hundred years time, never mind three hundred.'

'Apparently when Samuel Pepys had the builders in they shaved his dog and mixed his fur with the plaster,' I laugh.

'Good lord! The poor creature. Speaking of poor creatures, shouldn't we be letting the chickens out?'

'Okay, you do the chickens and I'll make breakfast.'

It's difficult to resist the eggs that were laid only the previous day so, by the time Rob reappears, there are two plates of fresh, golden-yellow scrambled eggs on toast ready on the table.

'Oh my, that looks good! They're an amazing colour aren't they? And you'll be pleased to know I just found four more,' he says setting the eggs down before settling down at the table. 'The girls are all out and I've fed them, but mind you that one with the scraggy neck's a nasty bit of goods. She had a go at me while I was trying to feed them. I was just getting a tissue out of my pocket when she leapt up and snatched it out of my hand!'

'Yes, I noticed she was a bit of a bully but the others seem to survive. I suppose that's what's meant by the pecking order. I've never really thought about it before. So what's the plan for the day?'

'I thought it might be nice to go and have a look at the church. It's supposedly got a fascinating history.'

'Okay, that sounds interesting. Then maybe we could go for a walk along the river after lunch if it isn't too muddy.'

'Sounds perfect, it'll be a joy to see a river again. I know we have the sea but it's just not the same.'

The church is, indeed, fascinating, with tombs of the local landed gentry and an ancient font. While I'm examining one of the elaborate tombs of the Scudamore family in the nave a door at the back of the church creaks open and a young woman appears who, we assume by her attire, must be the local vicar. As she walks towards us her long, red hair catches the light that is streaming through one of the stained-glass windows. She smiles warmly and comes over to greet us. I can't help but notice her pale complexion and somewhat doleful expression.

'Good morning! Isn't it a lovely day? Are you visiting?'

Rob explains what we're up to, staying in the village and house-sitting.

'Oh you must mean at the Jenkins' house. They're such a lovely family and Molly's just amazing. She comes to church with them every Sunday and just lies quietly in the pews. If Matthew needs to take his medication it's all very discreet. She's literally a Godsend.'

'Yes, it's a pity Molly didn't stay behind, we'd have loved to have had her company,' replies Rob.

'You can always come and take my dog out for a walk if you're in need of a friend,' she laughs, heading for the vestry. 'Anyhow, do excuse me, I've got a funeral this afternoon and need to prepare. Enjoy the rest of your stay!'

'Thank you,' we reply in unison and head out to the churchyard.

'Have you noticed the names here Chris?' calls Rob from behind a large, Victorian, marble gravestone. 'There are an awful lot of Welsh names. Griffiths, Jones, Watkins, Powell, Jenkins. I guess being so near the border a lot of Welsh people settled here.'

'Most probably. We can't be more than a few miles away. They probably came charging over the borders with their bows and arrows, pillaged the village and murdered a few Englishmen.'

'Speaking of which I could murder some lunch, shall we head home?'

'Good idea. I'm feeling peckish too.'

'As long as you don't start attacking me like that bad-tempered chicken! What's for lunch?'

'Well I guess we ought to try and use up some of the eggs so do you fancy an omelette?'

'Sounds wonderful. A glass of cider would go down well too!'

It's towards the end of the afternoon after a lovely walk by the river that we head over to the Post Office to send some postcards home. It's located in a beautiful old timber-framed building which lists dramatically towards the road, the lower part of the overhang just above head height. As a result the interior is quite dark but, as we head to the counter, we notice what looks like a small cushion by the service-hatch. On closer inspection we realise that it is, in fact, a very small Yorkshire Terrier curled up in a ball and clearly in a deep sleep. Not wanting to wake it up I smile at the elderly lady behind the screen and ask very quietly for the stamps that we need.

'Oh don't whisper on her account,' laughs the woman. 'She's as deaf as a doorpost.'

'She must be the quietest Yorkie I've ever come across,' replies Rob. 'Bless her, how old is she?'

'Nearly seventeen. She's actually the daughter of my previous Yorkie and she lived to eighteen.'

'My goodness. I didn't realise they could live that long. How wonderful and she's still got a lovely coat,' comments Rob.

'Well she's been on a special diet for the last two years. She hasn't got many teeth left. Costs me a fortune but it seems to have helped her coat, although it is getting a bit thin in places.'

'A bit like mine!' laughs Rob rubbing the top of his head. 'Anyhow, thank you for the stamps. Goodbye.'

It's just as we're leaving that who should come through the door but the vicar.

'Oh my goodness, the very people!' she smiles. 'Hello again. I was just on my way to see you. Have you got a moment?'

'Absolutely. How can we help?' asks Rob.

'Er, let's just step outside,' she says, glancing towards the lady behind the counter and walking back onto the pavement. 'I was wondering if you could possibly help us out on Saturday? The gentleman who was going to judge the dog-show is suddenly unavailable and we wondered if you would be willing to help with the judging? I mean your experience with house-sitting obviously means that you're familiar with a number of breeds so we thought it would be right up your street. It's nothing at all serious, just a bit of fun. So what do you think?'

I look at Rob with a slight panic in my eyes but before we've even managed to communicate he's already agreeing. 'Of course. We'd love to, wouldn't we darling?' he says, looking in my direction with a big smile on his face. 'Is this the show that raises money for Medical Detection Dogs?'

'That's right,' replies the vicar, 'we've all been so impressed by Molly and the change she's made to the Jenkins family that we like to offer some support. Oh that's wonderful! Thank you both so much. So, we'll see you on Saturday then. 2.30 start in the field next to the vicarage, I'll see you there!' And with that she ducks her head under the low beam above the door and goes back into the Post Office.

As soon as we're out of earshot I stop and turn to Rob. 'What on earth made you accept? We don't know the first thing about judging dogs.'

'She only asked us to help so there'll be other judges too and after all it is only a bit of fun and it's for a good cause.'

'I bet. I know these sort of events. They'll be deadly serious. I bet you any money that it'll turn nasty.'

'Oh don't be so silly Chris. It'll be a lovely chance to meet some more dogs and it'll just be a nice, friendly village get-together, so stop worrying.'

Saturday morning dawns faster than I'd expected. I can't pretend that I'm more than a little anxious about the dog-show but there doesn't seem to be any way of getting out of it. I reassure myself that it's a charity event and a good one at that. Rob arrives at the breakfast table looking rather dapper, his best chinos and brogues accessorised by a pin-striped open-necked shirt with a silk handkerchief tied at the neck.

'Going somewhere special darling?' I ask putting the coffee pot in front of him as he settles down at the table.

'Well I thought I ought to dress the part you know. After all we have standards to maintain as my good friend Ernest would have reminded me. And I did notice that you rather liked David's cravat,' he says, adjusting his handkerchief in the mirror.

'Yes but it is only a village do, it's not Crufts for goodness sake.'

'That is beside the point. They've been kind enough to ask us and I feel we ought to rise to the occasion. Anyhow, what's for breakfast?'

'Eggs.'

'Again? I've never eaten so many eggs in my life. I'll get egg-bound at this rate.'

'Don't be so silly. Humans don't get egg-bound, it's only birds.'

'My mother always said we'd become egg-bound if we ate too many and she was always right.'

'Well, much as I hate to criticise your mother, I think that on this occasion she was wrong. And if you don't stop moaning your breakfast'll be cold. Oh, and by the way there was a flyer through the letter-box this morning about the dog-show and it's got the classes on it.'

'Oh, and?' mumbles Rob, dipping his toast in the top of his boiled egg.

'Best girl; best boy; dog with the waggiest tail; golden oldie; the dog that looks most like its owner and best in show.'

'Well that sounds fairly straight forward.'

'I wish I shared your optimism. I actually feel quite nervous about it.'

'That's not like you darling,' says Rob, pouring me a large cup of coffee. 'You're usually the one propping me up. And as I said, they only asked us to help so there are bound to be other people judging. Just try and relax, I'm sure it'll be fun.'

As we approach the vicarage shortly after lunch there seems to be quite a crowd gathering in the field. It's a beautiful afternoon with the sun making the whole scene a veritable English picture-postcard. There's bunting outside the house and an array of refreshments laid out on trestle tables in a corner of the field. A make-shift ring has been constructed out of straw bales where some of the villagers have already parked themselves, enjoying cups of tea and generous slices of home-made cake. A number of dogs have already arrived and are being smartened up by their respective owners who seem to have come equipped with all manner of grooming kit.

'You see,' I say to Rob. 'I warned you that this would be a serious business. Look over there!' Standing on a wicker hamper is what appears to be a Shih Tzu with its hair in curlers, being brushed by a rather large lady in a tweed suit and brogues.

'Good grief, it's hard to know which end is which,' laughs Rob.

'I think you might soon discover that this is no laughing matter. I did warn you. And for heaven's sake don't go saying things like that to the owner.'

At that moment we narrowly escape being knocked over by a Lakeland terrier who seems to have escaped his owner and is zooming manically around the perimeter of the field. A lady in a very colourful dress rushes past, clearly trying to catch him but not having much success.

'Well, it's all excitement here isn't it! I assume we'll be starting soon,' says Rob, rubbing his hands together and looking round the field.

'I do hope so, I just want to get this over with.'

As I stand nervously surveying the gathering crowd a gentleman in a smart pin-striped suit and a bow-tie walks up to us, doffing his panama hat as he approaches. 'Good afternoon. Mr and Mrs Baird I believe? I'm Nigel Scudamore, pleased to meet you both. So kind of you to help us out at the last moment.'

'Our pleasure,' says Rob, shaking hands.

'Such a pity that Monty couldn't make it but he was called away to do a programme in India and had no choice but to cancel his engagement. Anyhow, we've got you two wonderful people instead. I'll just make an announcement and then we'll get started, I know the entrants are all very keen to get going.' And with that he picks up a large megaphone and walks into the centre of the make-shift ring. 'Good afternoon ladies and gentlemen and welcome to the annual village dog show. We're delighted to see so many of you here for this very special event. As you know all the money raised this afternoon will go to the wonderful Medical Detection Dogs Charity. Many of you will already be familiar with the work that they do in supporting people with all manner of illnesses. However, it may surprise you to know that the latest development has been extending their work into detecting malaria, prostate cancer and, most recently Covid viruses, all of which is a wonderful advance in the work of these amazing dogs. So do please make sure you buy some raffle tickets and indulge in some of the wonderful home-made cakes that the lovely ladies of our WI have made for us. Some of you will already be aware that unfortunately, our celebrity neighbour, Monty Don, who had kindly agreed to be our judge today, was sadly called away to record a new programme. However we are delighted to welcome Mr and Mrs Baird who are visiting the area and looking after Molly who, I realise, many of you know as a support dog. So, with no further ado, please welcome our judges to the ring.'

I can't believe what I've just heard. As Rob takes my arm and coaxes me into the show-ring I can feel my legs begin to shake. The crowd are clapping as we walk forward, Rob waving to the crowd as though he's a celebrity.

'I didn't realise he meant Monty Don,' I say in a loud whisper.

'Who's Monty Don?' asks Rob, smiling at the folk who have gathered around the ring.

'For heaven's sake, he's a really well-known TV presenter. He has a gardening programme and travels the world visiting important gardens. We're absolute nobodies by comparison, and where are the other judges? I thought we were just supposed to be helping?'

'I don't know darling but it looks as though we're on our own,' replies Rob under his breath.

'Now our first class is for the best girl, so if you'd like to bring your dogs into the ring we'll make a start,' calls our host through the megaphone. 'And it seems we have some lovely ladies here in the line-up. No Mrs Watkins, I was referring to the dogs,' he laughs as one of the owners gives a little wiggle.

An assortment of dogs is paraded into the ring, some of their owners clearly taking this all very seriously, others looking more relaxed and seemingly entering just for the fun. There's a pretty little wire haired fox terrier trotting daintily at her owner's side, looking up dotingly; an extremely beautiful golden retriever with a plumed tail who looks as though she's just been for a dig, judging by the mud on her paws; two very handsome Welsh terriers; a very pretty Lhasa Apso; a gorgeous Airedale with a floppy ear; a rather overweight chocolate Labrador and a very nervous greyhound.

'Oh gosh, this is going to be tricky,' I whisper behind my hand. 'Let's go and talk to the owners,' I suggest. And so, one by one we make our way up the line asking the owners about their animal. Each one has its own story which only succeeds in making our job even more difficult. It seems that the terriers are mother and daughter, both clearly in excellent health and enjoying the excitement of the day. The Labrador clearly needs some exercise but her owner obviously has mobility problems and, knowing how much Labradors like their grub, it must be difficult for this loveable bundle to get the amount of exercise she needs.

'What's her name?' asks Rob, fondling the dog's head.

'Rolo,' replies the rather stout lady who is steadying herself on a colourful walking-stick. 'I know she's carrying a bit of weight but I had a hip operation a few months ago and it's been a long time healing. I'm afraid she isn't getting the amount of walks she used to have.'

'Well she's very lovely all the same,' replies Rob, clearly charming the owner.

Next in line is the rather skittish, nervous greyhound called Whisper who has beautiful lines and an elegant head. We discover that she's a retired racing dog who apparently took a long time to settle in her new home but who is now very much part of the family.

'She's a lovely looking dog,' I say to her owner, a young man who seems to be finding the event a little overwhelming.

'Thank you,' he replies, his eyes looking firmly at the ground.

'And good for you for taking her on. She clearly deserved a good home,' says Rob.

The young man blushes as we move on to the next entrant, the Golden Retriever. We walk up to her owner and it's while Rob is asking her some questions that I suddenly catch the dog's name. Nellie. Could it be? I wait until Rob's finished his conversation and, bending down to make a fuss of the dog comment on her muddy paws.

'Been doing a spot of gardening has she?' I ask, smiling up at her owner.

'I'm afraid so,' she replies. 'I'm going to have to repair the damage before a certain somebody finds out what she's been up to.'

I laugh and walk off to join Rob who's clearly deliberating. 'Well I don't know about you but I think the Retriever should win,' he says quietly.

'But she can't,' I say firmly.

'What do you mean can't? She's a beautiful animal and deserves to win.'

'I know, but she also happens to be Monty Don's dog, Nellie. She's a TV celebrity, Rob. She's got a twitter following of over twenty thousand. They'll think it's a fix or that we're star-struck or something.'

'Oh crikey, so what do we do now?'

'We choose somebody else,' I say, turning towards the crowd and smiling. 'They're all waiting so we'd better make our minds up quickly.'

'Okay, so who do you reckon?'

'I'd go for the greyhound. When you consider the life journey that that dog's had she deserves to win.'

'Okay, I'm happy with that. Let's go for it.'

Her owner, although acutely embarrassed, is clearly delighted to be awarded the red rosette, as is Whisper who bounds around him excitedly trying to take hold of it. Fortunately the crowd seems to be happy with our choice and gives him a warm round of applause.

The next three classes seem to go quite well, although a line-up of terriers in the best boy group causes a bit of a barking match. The wayward Lakeland terrier has obviously been caught and is standing next to another Lakie, an equally cheeky chappie. A beautiful spaniel with a silky black coat has obviously had a long day and has decided to have a nap, even refusing to be woken up by his owner proffering treats. However, my eye is immediately on two gorgeous Newfoundlands who stand quietly, drooling contentedly, one with a wonderful dark coat, the other black and white with spotty paws. I can't resist a hug with the dogs and a chat with the owners. It's hard to believe that both dogs are still puppies but already weighing in at 60 kilos!

It's a difficult decision, but the Lakeland terrier with the slightly wonky tail takes third prize with the spaniel a close second. However, the best boy goes to the adorable black Newfie called George, a big bear of a dog with a thick coat, a mane like a lion and paws the size of dinner-plates. He proves to have a really gentle nature and is every inch a champion in spite of the slobber.

'Well let's face it, the others didn't stand a chance once you'd set eyes on the Newfies Chris. I think it was a very biased decision on behalf of the judge.'

'But he's absolutely adorable and in such beautiful condition and he's such a sweetheart. He deserved to win.'

'I don't think the bloke with the Airedale was too impressed. Apparently his dog was sired by a Crufts champion.'

'Yes, but this isn't Crufts. It's a chance for the also-rans to win. Anyhow, we're keeping everyone waiting.'

Beginning to get into the swing of things we attempt to assume the poses that we've observed the judges make at dog-shows on the television, holding a hand to our chin and looking studiously at the dogs before going and chatting with the owner. The waggiest tail goes to a dear little Cairn terrier who trots around with his owner with what can only be described as a smile on his face looking full of fun. The golden oldie prize goes to the Yorkshire terrier owned by the lady at the post office who is clearly absolutely delighted.

'You see, I told you it would be okay,' says Rob reassuringly. 'So what's next?'

'I think it's the dog that looks most like its owner. This could be tricky, I mean we don't want to offend anyone.'

'No, but the fact that they've entered implies that they accept that they look like their dog in the first place, so I don't think we need to worry.'

As Mr Scudamore announces the class, the entrants process into the ring, led by the landlord from the pub with Winston the bulldog. It's only now that we realise how alike they are. Seeing them together emphasises the stocky build, short legs and jowled features shared by dog and master. They're closely followed by the vicar who is leading a handsome red setter, its feathered tail flowing handsomely as it extends its legs, holding its head up proudly. Next is a tall lady with long blonde hair leading an Afghan hound. They seem to have the same facial expression, a slightly haughty, sophisticated look, as they make their way around the show-ring. A sallow-skinned gentleman with short, dark, curly hair follows behind leading a curly-coated retriever, a breed that I've read about but never seen, man and dog forming a handsome pair. Lastly comes a white, standard poodle led by an elderly lady wearing a twin-set and pearls whose hair has been styled in a tight perm.

After much deliberation we award the prize to the pub landlord which seems to go down well with the crowd. Hopefully we're now in his favour as he shakes us firmly by the hand and waves the rosette in the air as he leaves the ring.

'Well that was a relief!' says Rob under his breath. 'It could have been a tricky one.'

'Yes, but we've still got best in show,' I reply, quietly worried about the outcome of the final class.

Mr Scudamore returns to announce the last class and the contestants are led into the ring by their proud owners. There's quite a crowd gathered and we sense that there's a lot of whispering going on between the observers. Into the ring come our five winners: the greyhound, the Newfie, the Cairn, the Yorkie and the bulldog. You couldn't have chosen a more diverse mix if you'd tried and I find it hard to suppress a giggle. The Yorkie rears up in her little harness and yaps incessantly at the Newfie. The lady from the Post Office has no success in trying to stop her and becomes more and more flustered, looking apologetically in our direction. However, unperturbed by the attempted attack, George simply lies down with his head on his paws and gives a loud sigh as if in exasperation. The Cairn continues to wag his tail furiously and looks endearingly at his owner. The pub landlord is clearly hoping he's in for first prize as he's standing there with his chest puffed out with a large toothy smile looking even more like his dog than ever. Our young man on the other hand looks as though he wants the ground to swallow him up as he stands there biting his lip, eyes blinking.

'So who's it going to be?' asks Rob, holding his hand over his mouth. 'It's a tough one isn't it?'

'Mmm. It is but I know who I think should win,' I reply quietly.

'Let me guess, he's got huge paws and a load of slobber down his front.'

'Actually no. I'm going for the greyhound.'

'Well good for you!' he says turning towards me. 'She'd have been my choice too. That young man's done so well to win her over and I bet they're good for each other. Decision made!' And with that Rob looks over at Mr Scudamore and gives him the thumbs up.

'Well ladies and gentlemen, it appears that we have a decision from our judges,' comes the voice over the megaphone. 'And the winner of the Best in Show is …'

As we walk towards the young man to present the trophy he begins shaking his head in disbelief and as Rob holds out his hand to congratulate him he's clearly holding back the tears. I can feel myself welling up but, as Rob takes the young man's arm to reassure him, Whisper jumps up at her owner and, with her paws on his chest, begins licking his face. The crowd is clearly behind our decision as there is a generous round of applause as the young man takes the trophy and holds it up for all to see.

Mr Scudamore comes walking over to thank us. 'We can't thank you enough. You've done a splendid job and everyone seems happy, especially young James. An excellent choice if I may say so.'

'It's been our pleasure,' replies Rob, 'and hopefully you've made plenty of money for the charity.'

'I'm sure we will have. It's good to be able to support such a worthwhile cause. Thank you again and I hope you enjoy the rest of your stay.' And with that he heads off into the crowd.

'Well I don't know about you, darling, but I could murder a pint of cider. Let's wander over to the pub and hope that matey's still speaking to us!'

It's quite late the following morning when we surface, the excitement of the previous day having caught up with us. Rob pops out to feed the chickens while I make a pot of strong coffee. He returns clutching three brown eggs in his outstretched hands.

'More for the collection I'm afraid, darling. I think Chicken Vindaloo is responsible for two of them.'

'Chicken Vindaloo,' I laugh, 'where did you get that one from?'

'It's the feisty one with the scraggy neck. She's a bit hot-tempered isn't she? Poor old Chicken Tikka seems quite intimidated by her.'

'You shouldn't give them names, you'll get too attached to them,' I laugh, settling down at the table. 'And come and sit down before your breakfast gets cold.'

'And dare I ask what we're having?'

'Silly question and you know it. They're poached and the toast is some of that lovely wholemeal bread from the village bakery.'

'I shouldn't complain, they are delicious but they're laying them faster than we can eat them. I guess the Jenkins usually give them away or even sell them.'

'Quite possibly,' I reply, cutting into the egg yolk and watching it run into the toast. 'Anyhow, what's on the itinerary today Mr B?'

'I thought that maybe we could go for a drive and explore the border country. See if we can spot any marauding Welshmen.'

'Sounds good to me. I'll give the chicken coop a clean and then we could go any …'

I'm interrupted by a loud knock on the front door.

'Probably the postman,' says Rob, rising from his chair. 'Don't worry, I'll go.'

I can hear a conversation going on but I'm not sure who Rob's talking to.

'No, that's really kind of you, but there really was no need, we had a lovely afternoon. I'm sure Chris will be delighted. We'll maybe see you around before we leave? Yes, thank you so much. Goodbye.'

'So who was it?' I call through to the porch.

'The vicar,' replies Rob, coming back into the kitchen. 'She brought us a little thank you present for helping them out.'

'Oh, that was kind of her, so what have we got?'

'A flagon of local cider, a fruit cake and half a dozen duck eggs,' replies Rob. 'Fancy an omelette for lunch?'

WHAT'S IN A NAME?

'You seem busy darling,' comments Rob, looking up from his crossword. 'Who are you writing to?'

'I'm not,' I reply.

'Okay. So what are you writing? Another article for the Parish Magazine?'

'No, I'm writing a book, and I'd appreciate it if you didn't keep interrupting me,' I reply looking fixedly at my laptop.

Obviously taken aback by my reply, Rob drops his newspaper and gives me a quizzical look.

'A book?'

'Yes, that's what I said.'

'That's a bit ambitious isn't it?'

'I don't know until I've tried but I thought it was worth having a stab at it.'

'So what's it about? Dormer windows of the Channel Islands? The folklore of Guernsey?'

'No, it's a novel.'

'Good grief! This is a new departure. So have you started on that children's book you've been threatening to write all these years?'

'No, it's not a children's book. I've decided to write about our house-sitting experiences.'

'Oh my! That's a brilliant idea! We've certainly had some adventures. But you're not going to write it in an autobiographical way, are you?'

'Well, sort of. I'm going to use our experiences but fictionalise it.'

'But we won't be us will we? I mean I wouldn't want anyone reading about me Chris, it's too personal.'

'No, I told you, it's a novel, not an autobiography. I'm going to base my story on some of the things that have happened to us but it's going to be a fictitious couple, not us.'

'So you won't use my name?'

'No, I'm going to call you something else.'

'Like what?'

'I don't know yet and I do wish you wouldn't keep talking. It interrupts my train of thought.'

'How about Philip? I always wanted to be called Philip.'

'No, it's too sophisticated.'

'What do you mean?'

'It's just got that ring to it. No you need to be a Bob or Bill or Jim or something, a bit more user-friendly.'

'Hugh?'

'No.'

'William?'

'No. Rob, will you please leave me alone? I can't concentrate with you rabbiting on.'

'Well I do think there should be an element of choice in all this. People are bound to know it's me really.'

'People are not. The reader won't have a clue who you are.'

'That may be the case but what about friends and family?'

'If they recognise any of your characteristics they'll just have a jolly good laugh.'

'Yes, but that's what I'm worried about.'

'I've got it!'

'What?'

'Your name.'

'So what's it going to be?'

'I'm not telling you.'

'Oh Chris that is so unfair.'

'No it's not, you'll only moan.'

'But you will make me handsome won't you? You know, tall, tanned and sophisticated, greying a little at the temples.'

'Rob, for the nth time it's not you and if you keep on disturbing me I shall make my character into a short, balding man with a beer-belly.'

'Oh alright I'll be quiet.'

I return to my imaginary world for no more than a couple of minutes before I'm interrupted yet again.

'So what are these two going to get up to?'

'Well, as I said, I'm going to base it on some of the things that have really happened to us. I thought I could write about that time you kept watering the house-plants in the house in Cambridge before you realised they were all artificial. Do you remember? The water was overflowing onto the window-sills in great puddles before you realised. Oh, and when you got dragged down the road by the bulldog when he chased the badger, that was so funny,' I laugh recollecting the image.

'I don't think I like the sound of this at all Chris. It seems you're just out to make me look like a fool and that's most unfair. No doubt you're going to be the sensible one in all this?'

'Of course.'

'So what are you going to be called?'

'I was thinking Julia, or maybe Claudia, you know, something with a bit of sophistication.'

'Oh so you're going to be sophisticated and I'm going to be Bob the builder, that's nice,' moans Rob looking somewhat disgruntled and stomping off into the kitchen. I've no sooner written a couple of sentences and he's back.

'So if this is fiction that means you can create a few scenes doesn't it, I mean they don't all have to be based on real happenings?'

'No, but I think I'd write more convincingly about something I've actually experienced.'

'So no car chases then?'

'No, no car chases.'

'No shootouts?'

'No.'

'But can you man me up a bit? After all, I should be the one who sorts out all the problems.'

'But you do, with superglue, Blu Tac or WD40.'

'That's not what I mean and you know it, only I don't want to come across as a wimp.'

'Rob, I don't know how many more times I have to tell you that this is not about you. It may be based on experiences we've had together but Terry is not you and you are not Terry.'

'Terry? You mean you've called me Terry? How could you Chris? That's a really wet sort of name. This gets more unfair by the minute.'

'Well I wanted something that was a shortened version of something so that Julia could berate him by calling him Terence.'

'Well I'm sorry but I really don't think that's funny. I'm going to be the laughing stock,' says Rob sulkily and looking wounded.

'It's either Terry or Dave, I'll let you choose,' I smirk.

'Oh no, this is just getting worse. I'll let you choose, after all it is your book, but promise me you'll write a disclaimer in the introduction?'

'I might, but it'll cost you Mr Baird,' I smile, leaning back in my chair.

'How much?'

'A smacker of a kiss and a glass of wine.'

At which 'Terry' heads for the kitchen and returns with two glasses, a corkscrew and a bottle of Malbec.

ACKNOWLEDGEMENTS

MY THANKS GO TO all those readers who have encouraged me to write the sequel to *Barking Mad: Confessions of a Dog-Sitter*. It's been fun to recall some of the mad adventures that my husband and I have had whilst house-sitting. Our thanks go to all the lovely people who have welcomed us into their homes and let us share their furry families. We have taken away fond memories of every house-sit and have made many lasting friendships along the way. Whilst the episodes in this book have been inspired by some of the adventures that we have had, the owners, animals and houses are purely fictitious.

Special thanks go to Steve Foote of Blue Ormer Publishing for arranging the book ready for publication; to the super-talented Iain Welch for his wonderful illustrations; Helen Boden for helping me get my parrot facts correct; Barbara Santi for help with my Italian; Paula Ohlbrock for help with my German and to the lovely staff at Medical Detection Dogs for their expertise. Find out more about their amazing work at their website medicaldetectiondogs.org.uk. You can even sponsor a puppy!

For those of you who yearn for a dog of your own, then look no further than Twitter where people all over the world share the joy of dog-ownership. I thank them all for their generosity but especially their compassion in supporting one another through difficult times.

Last but by no means least, to my husband, Richard, (who continues to deny any resemblance to Rob) for sharing the adventures, and for supporting me throughout the writing process with his eagle-eye, gentle criticism and endless encouragement.

Jane Mosse 2022

ENDAWGSMENTS

We Lakeland Terriers love adventures, so it was a delight to relax with a whole book of escapades after a hard day's play. Pet sitters Chris and Rob get to visit fabulous places where they are supervised by fellow dogs, cats (grrrr) and even a mischievous parrot! Look out for the village dog show where I'm sure I spotted several of my pals wooing the locals. Be more terrier by joining me in a thoroughly entertaining read!

Archie Lakeland @ArchieLakeland

We loved the first book and can't wait for Dad to read this one to us. It may even have newfydoofs in it but Dad says that's top secret and you'll have to read it and find out. Me and Cookie said we'd like Chris and Rob to come and look after us, I think we'd get lots of cuddles and treats. But for now we're going to settle down and wait for this next wonderful instalment.

Bandit and Cookie @montydogge

As a rather old Wire Haired Fox Terrier – and a spinster of this parish – this book took me to countries I thought I'd never visit again, and made my grey fur ripple with the giggles I had with each chapter.

Every adventure makes you feel you're there with Rob and Chris, encouraging them to embrace new cultures, food and friends - and not be outwitted by the animals in their care. This is a book you can pick up time and time again and lose yourself in the stories with a guaranteed smile and an admiration for us furry companions. I'd definitely book them if I ever needed looking after (just remember to stock up on a bottle of wine or two, or three!)

Freckles Chimes @FrecklesChimes

ABOUT THE AUTHOR

JANE MOSSE was born in Newcastle-Upon-Tyne where she was awarded the title of Freeman of the City and, as a result, has the right to graze her cow on the town moor. (She has yet to get the cow). She began her writing career as a researcher for *Nicholson's Guide to the Waterways* alongside developing her love of poetry. In 2018 she published her first collection of poems, *Guernsey Legends*, in partnership with local artist Frances Lemmon.

Stark Raving Bonkers is her second novel and was inspired by some of the adventures that she and her husband Richard have had since taking up house-sitting. They live on the beautiful island of Guernsey in the Channel Islands.

IAIN WELCH is an artist and illustrator living in rural North Herefordshire. He spends most of his time drawing, walking and cuddling dogs.

More information about him can be found at iainwelch.co.uk.

BARKING MAD!

BARKING MAD!

Confessions of a Dog-Sitter
JANE MOSSE

Barking Mad:Confessions of a Dog-Sitter was Jane's first novel, inspired by the experiences that she and her husband, Richard, have had since taking up house-sitting in their retirement. In 2021 it was short-listed for the BookBrunch Selfie's Award for Autobiography and Memoir.

What readers say:

'"Barking Mad" is more than just a good read – it is one of those that 'sticks to you' kind of good read. You won't want the pages to stop turning. And at the end, you will be looking for more.'

Rebecca Holland

'Travel, plus animals, plus nosing about in other people's houses? It's a perfect formula for an enjoyably escapist read.'

Peter Kenny

'The stories are so funny. I treat myself to a chapter every few days. Iain's illustrations are perfect.'

Andrea Miller (on Twitter)

'The characters they meet on their travels – both human, canine, feline and more – and the adventures they experience, some laugh out loud funny, others more challenging, are what makes this book so readable.'

Your Dog Magazine

HOLLY

Waking, my hand falls on warm fur:
a small ribcage rising, falling,
as breath goes on doing its work.

We are connected, she to me,
by synchronous breathing; by love,
on my part; on hers, obedience.

Now fifteen years, I hold her close,
gently as when she was a pup,
skin-and-bones, promising nothing.

A good dog, demanding only
a clean, warm bed; small kindnesses.
Fortune, grant her sleep, untroubled.

RUFUS

Such strength of body, such a noble head;
expressive eyes like pathways to the soul,
but dominant, reluctant to be led,
determined to assume the Alpha role.

You were a fierce and charismatic lad
yet butter-soft when seeking a caress.
Some wisdom, beyond canine sense, you had.
We miss you and your brutish gentleness.

Richard Fleming
redhandwriter.blogspot.com